SCHOLASTIC
COLLECTIONS
Compiled by Peter Morrell

Carols

D0654295

Published by Scholastic Publications Ltd,
Villiers House,
Clarendon Avenue,
Leamington Spa,
Warwickshire CV32 5PR

Compiler Peter Morrell
Editors Margaret Christie and Christine Lee
Series designer Joy White
Designer Micky Pledge
Cover illustration Gini Wade
Illustrations Sue Woollatt

Designed using Aldus Pagemaker
Processed by Pages Bureau, Leamington Spa
Artwork by David Harban Design, Warwick
Music typesetting by W.A. Pitt (Musical Services)
Printed in Great Britain by Ebenezer Baylis & Son, Worcester

British Library Cataloguing-in-Publication Data
A catalogue record for this book is
available from the British Library.

ISBN 0-590-53306-1

Contents

THE CHRISTMAS STORY

THE CHRISTMAS MESSAGE

CHRISTMAS AROUND THE WORLD

CHRISTMAS AT HOME AND SCHOOL

Acknowledgements

The publishers gratefully acknowledge permission to reproduce the following copyright material:

©1994 Clive Barnwell for 'A star is shining', 'If I stay awake', 'If they give me peace for Christmas', 'I hope Santa Claus will come tonight', 'Flavour of Christmas', 'Follow that star', 'Frosty', 'Ride little donkey', 'So long ago', 'Starlight', 'That first Christmas night', 'The message' and 'Wishing you all a Merry Christmas'; ©1994 Ann Bryant for 'Alle jahre wieder', 'Christmas daydreams', 'Christmas pictures in the fire', 'Christmas squiggles', 'Father Christmas rock around Europe', 'Hoe leit dit Kindeken', 'Il est né le divin Enfant', 'Jeg er saa glad hver jukelveld', 'Juletraeet med sin pynt', 'One little thing', 'So long ago', 'The Christmas train', 'The robin' and 'You must go Mary'; ©1994 Debbie Campbell for 'A Christmas dream', 'Christmas time is here', 'I can't get to sleep', 'I wish I was a shepherd', 'My gran wants an Action Man', 'Was it an angel?' and 'Welcome to the world (Mary's song)'; ©1994 Elizabeth Chapman for 'New Year' (words only); ©1984 Douglas Coombes for 'Across the nations' (music only); ©1994 Lesley Funge for 'Child in the manger', 'Christmas around the world', 'If I'd been born in Bethlehem' and 'Sweet baby of mine'; ©1994 Jean Gilbert for 'The animals' Christmas song'; ©1994 Gerald Haigh for 'The aid worker's Christmas' and 'The golden star'; ©1994 Carole Henderson Begg for 'If Jesus was born today' and 'Whispering winds'; ©1987 Ian Henderson Begg for 'O Mister Builder (Santa's song)', ©1988 Ian Henderson Begg for 'A gift for a King', ©1992 Ian Henderson Begg for 'Christmas ringers', ©1994 Ian Henderson Begg for 'Baby Jesus, lying in a stall', 'Candle bright', 'Christmas down in the market square', 'Christmas on the beach', 'Christmas pudding song', 'Christmas thoughts', 'Comin' to dis world', 'Decorate the tree', 'Hurry away' and 'The stranger in the blizzard'; ©1987 Lonee Hewitt for 'Join hands', ©1989 Lonee Hewitt for 'Sing joy', ©1992 Lonee Hewitt for 'Noel, Noel' and 'Starry nights' and ©1994 Lonee Hewitt for 'We wish you a Merry Christmas; ©1988 Graham Kendrick for 'O come and join the dance', 'The candle song', 'The Christmas Child', and 'This Child' and ©1993 Graham Kendrick for 'You came from the highest' by permission of Make Way Music, PO Box 263, Croydon, Surrey SR9 5AP; ©1981 Richard Llewellyn for 'Joyeux Noel' (RVL Wilderness Music); ©1994 Lisa MacKenzie for 'After-dinner lament', 'Buying presents', 'Christmas bells', 'Dear Santa Claus', 'The brightest star', 'The real Christmas' and 'Three great kings'; ©1994 Nash Meghji for 'Issa Alei Salaam'; ©1994 Catherine Morrell for 'Worlds apart'; ©1994 Peter Morrell for 'Bethlehem boy', 'Christmas tree', 'Heaven on earth', 'New Year' (music only), 'Ring out those bells for Him', 'Stars shine bright' and 'We want to see what's goin' on!'; ©1994 David Moses for 'An old man lives in Lollipop Land', 'Aren't you glad they've cancelled Christmas?', 'Christmas shopping', 'Christmas tree', 'Come shepherd, come', 'My name is Father Christmas', 'Rock a little baby' and 'What is all the noise about?'; ©1994 Gillian Parker for 'Christmas bells', 'Christmas card', 'Christmas market', 'The bells ring out', 'The carol singers', 'The stable door' and 'The troubadour's carol'; ©1994 Jonathan Pudsey for 'Jesus came that night'; ©1994 David Selwyn for 'The colours of Mary'; ©1984 Fiona Shore for 'Across the nations' (words only); ©1994 Alan Simmons for 'Christmas time', 'Lullaby', 'Round the Christmas tree', 'Snowflakes', 'The bells of Bethlehem' and 'Three wise men'; ©1994 Paul Sudlow for 'No room blues' and 'The Christmas alphabet'; and ©1994 Chris Williams for 'Merry Christmas and a Happy New Year' and 'The Nth day of Christmas'.

Every effort has been made to trace copyright holders for material in this anthology and the publishers apologise for any inadvertent omissions.

INTRODUCTION

Christmas is a time of wonder and excitement, holidays and hope, turkey and traditions. One of the main traditions of Christmas time is the singing of carols. Whether they are sung formally to accompany nine lessons or as part of a nostalgic annual pilgrimage to Midnight Mass, in a school production or assembly or simply sung at home, carols are now an integral part of Christmas.

However, the importance of carols within the celebration of Christmas was not always such, for originally a carol was a song that accompanied a dance. It may well have its derivation in the Old French word for a dance, *carole*, and thus have no obvious link with Christmas. In fact, it is unlikely that the early carols had anything to do with the Christian Church for their origins were in secular songs often relating to pagan themes.

Then in the thirteenth century, St Francis of Assisi introduced the crib depicting the Nativity scene, complete with people, ox and ass. To this were added songs to accompany the Crib Service and also to help the audience to participate in and understand the mystery. And so developed the link between songs (carols) and the story of Christmas.

The early Crib Services may well have been held out of doors, and so the idea of carols being sung outside has gradually developed through the centuries. At one time this was known as wassailing (*was haile* meaning 'your health' was a Saxon drinking toast) when a group of singers (waits) would travel from town to town singing songs of good wishes. Today's carol singers continue this tradition, although their wassailing is restricted to house-to-house and street-to-street rather than town-to-town.

It was during Queen Victoria's reign that the traditions of Christmas that we recognise and perpetuate today were given respectability. The Christmas tree with its lights and decorations, the giving and receiving of presents and the singing of carols all became an integral part of Christmas.

In this collection of carols, I have taken Isaacs and Martin's* definition as a carol being 'any printed song suitable for Christmas'. The collection, which is divided into four sections, covers the many aspects of the Christmas story as well as the more peripheral side of Christmas, such as robin redbreasts in snowy scenes, decorated trees and, of course, Santa Claus.

The first section, 'The Christmas story', comprises carols relating specifically to the birth of Jesus. It is arranged in the generally agreed order of events and, with a number of carols for each event, the permutations for a Carol Service are quite considerable.

The second section takes as its theme 'The Christmas message' of love, peace, caring and sharing, and provides material to complement a selection from section one.

**Dictionary of Music*, edited by Isaacs and Martin, first published in 1982 by Hamlyn

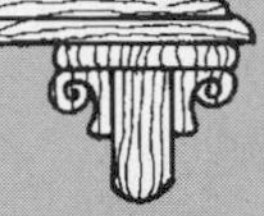

Section three covers 'Christmas around the world', a popular theme for a school's presentation, and includes carols which have been specially translated for this collection as well as a beautiful Hindi carol, again specially written.

The final section is a miscellany of carols for 'Christmas at home and school', including such topics as Santa Claus, snowflakes, buying presents and, naturally in a collection of carols, a song about carol singers!

With so many new and specially commissioned carols, this collection will provide a refreshing alternative to the traditional carols and will be a valuable resource for those involved in the selection and singing of carols. The pages of this book are photocopiable, so the children will benefit from seeing the 'whole carol', rather than just the words or hearing and repeating. There is a considerable variety of styles and much scope for part singing.

To the many contributors who have made their material available for this collection, my grateful thanks. I'm sure many of these carols will become firm favourites.

A happy, peaceful and musical Christmas!

Peter Morrell

THE CHRISTMAS STORY

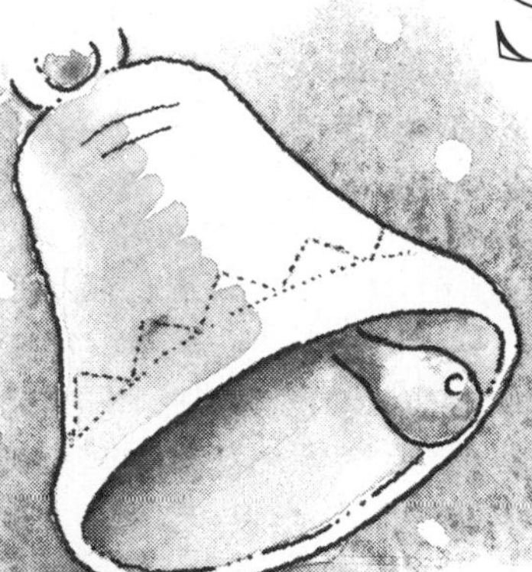

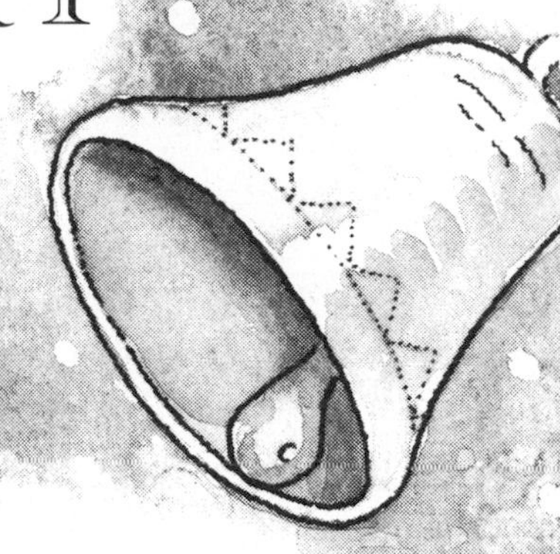

The bells of Bethlehem

Alan Simmons

The colours of Mary

David Selwyn

2.To Bethlehem went Mary
Riding on donkey grey:
'O sweet donkey, carry me gently,
You bear a King today.
One day in the future
Again He'll ride on thee;
Donkey, with your coat so grey,
Blessed may you be!'

3.A star shone over Mary,
Golden and high and bright,
And the stable it lit with splendour
Where Jesus was born that night.
Mary said, 'The heavens
Are glorious as can be!
Golden star, for shining so,
Blessed may you be!'

4.The shepherds heard of Mary
Huddled all on the green;
And the Wise Men came from their kingdoms,
Where shrill-voiced peacocks scream.
Mary said, 'These sages
Will pass a holy tree;
Green tree that is growing still,
Blessed may you be!'

5.Then Mary sat in the stable,
White was the robe she wore;
And the kings knelt by her in homage,
The shepherds looked in at the door.
Mary said, 'This Baby
Is born in purity;
White and perfect innocence,
Blessed may you be!'

6.And we must be like Mary,
Spotless and full of grace,
So that we can go to the stable
And enter the holy place.
Mary, our lives are coloured
With blissful thoughts of thee;
Gentle Mother of Our Lord,
Blessed may you be!

Was it an angel?

Debbie Campbell

2. A gentle voice called out to me
And told me where to find
A baby who was born to be
The saviour of mankind.

You must go, Mary

Ann Bryant

G
A7
D
D.𝄋 to ⊕ then Coda
one they are clos - ing doors till the morn - ing light.
You must
Coda (D)
G
D
And it's a long hard jour - ney and you're oh so
G
Em
wea - ry And ev - 'ry - where you go, they turn you a -
A
G
D
-way. Yes it's a long hard jour - ney and you're oh so
A
A7
D
wea - ry, Will you ev - er find some - where to stay?

Ride little donkey

Clive Barnwell

Chorus:
(D) E♭ (G) A♭ (A) B♭ (D) E♭ (G) A♭ (A) B♭ (D) E♭
Ride lit - tle don - key, ride, ride, ride. You've got to get to Beth - le - hem.
Though lit - tle don - key you are tired, you can have rest and wa - ter then.
(A) B♭ (D) E♭ (A) B♭ (D) E♭
E - ven if it's a long, long way, Ma - ry has had a wear - y day.
(A) B♭ (D) E♭ (A) B♭
Beth - le - hem can't be far a - way and there you'll find a place to stay. So
1.
ride lit - tle don - key, ride, ride, ride. You've got to get to Beth - le - hem.
2.
You've got to get to Beth - le - hem.

No room blues

Paul Sudlow

1,3,4.
2.
B♭7 F C7 F C7♯5
They got the No Room Blues.
lose, lose, lose, They got the No Room Blues.
F A7/E Dm F/C F B♭
3. Some - one, some - where, must have a place to
Ah Ah
F F/E Dm Am Dm7 G7
stay. Some - one, some - where, don't let it be this
Ah Ah
C F F/E F7/E♭ D♭7
way. Some - one, some - where, can't you see the state she's
Ah Ah Ah
F Am Dm7 G7
in? Nine months gone, no place to stay, it real - ly is a
Ah Ah Ah

C7sus4 C7 F F/E F7/E♭ D♭7
sin! Some - one, some - where they are not to blame! There
Ah Ah Ah
F/C Bm♭5 Am Dm Dm/C B♭ D.𝄋
must be some - one out there – this is - n't just a game.
rit.
Ah Ah, this is - n't just a game.
Coda
E♭dim C7/E F F E♭ F
start - ed to un - pack. Good - bye to No Room Blues Good - bye to
F Gm7 C7 F F E♭ F
No Room Blues Good - bye to No Room Blues
Gm7 Gm7/C C9♯5 F
Good - bye No Room Blues! and that's that.

2.Mary and Joseph they were tired and sore.
They were getting desperate, they couldn't take no more.
They went from joint to joint, but soon they got the point –
'No Vacancies' was hung outside of ev'ry door.

Chorus

3.Mary and Joseph thought they'd better quit, the
Last bus back to Nazareth was leaving in a bit.
They tried just one more place, you shoulda seen their face –
Just when they thought they'd missed the boat they scored a hit!

Chorus:
Now ain't that real good news? (*echo*)
Now ain't that real good news? (*echo*)
A roof above their head, (*echo*)
Some straw to make a bed, (*echo*)
They got no more to lose. (A case of can't refuse)
Goodbye to No Room Blues. (*both*)

4.Not much to look at, just a little shack,
Tucked around the corner in the car park at the back.
No longer had to roam, they'd found a home sweet home,
So in they went and shut the door and started to unpack.
Goodbye to No Room Blues. Goodbye to No Room Blues.
Goodbye to No Room Blues. Goodbye to No Room Blues! And that's that.

Candle bright

Ian Henderson Begg

2.Stable bare
No-one there,
Ox and ass just stand and stare
At the baby, child yet king;
Such a blessed sight.

3.Holy one,
God's own son,
Sent to earth, thy will be done.
Promised saviour, come to us;
Such a blessed sight.

4.Candle bright
Shed your light
Round the world this Christmas night.
Shine your gentle light of love;
Such a blessed sight.

The troubadour's carol

Gillian Parker

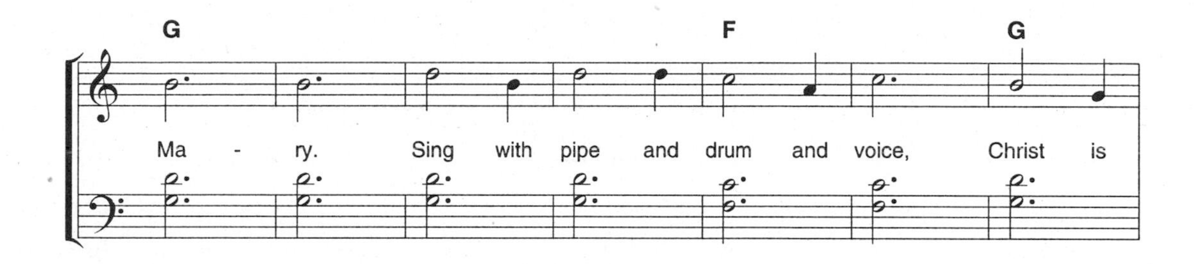

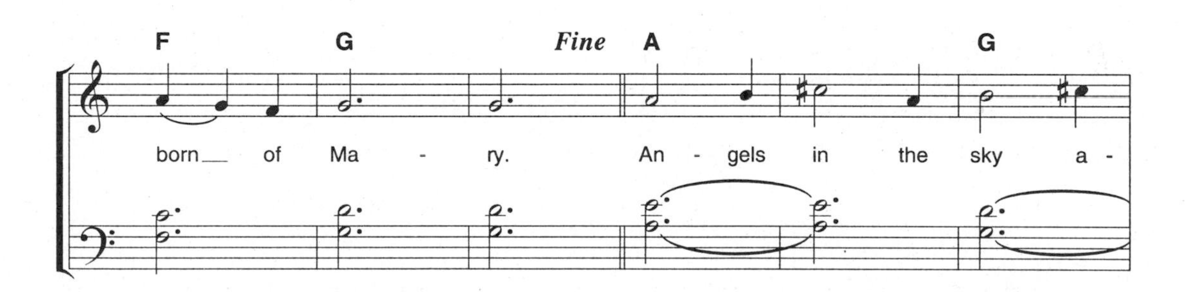

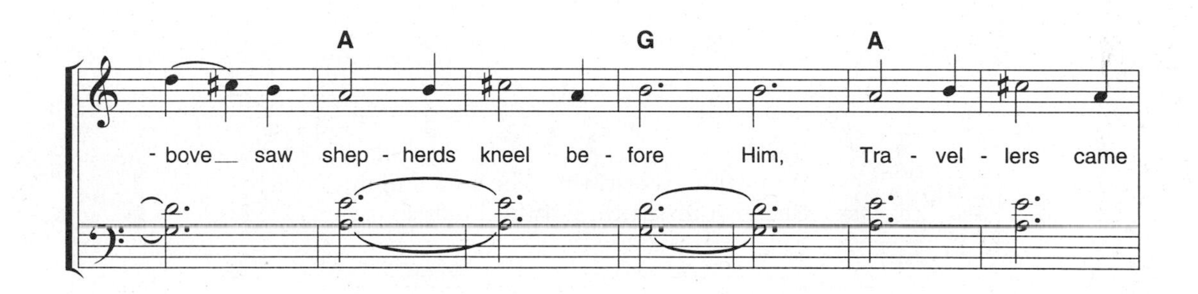

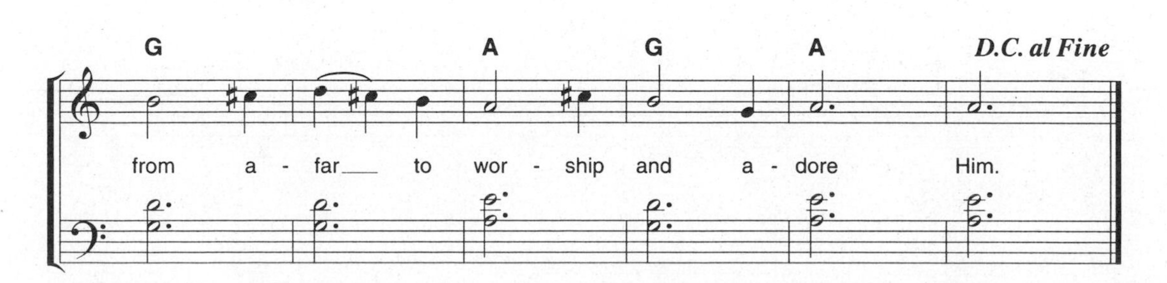

This Child

Graham Kendrick

2.This Child, rising on us like the sun,
Oh this Child, given to light everyone,
Oh this Child, guiding our feet on the pathway
To peace on earth.

3.This Child, raising the humble and poor,
Oh this Child, making the proud ones to fall;
This Child, filling the hungry with good things,
This heavenly Child.

That first Christmas night

Clive Barnwell

D Bm G A D Bm G A
win - ter. They did - n't sing of snow. They did - n't sing of
D Bm G Em A
pre - sents That night long a - -go. The song they sang was
D Bm G A D Bm G A
glo - ry. The song they sang was light. The song they sang was
1. 2.
D G Em A D D
won - der That first Christ - mas night. night.

Sweet baby of mine (Mary's song)

Lesley Funge

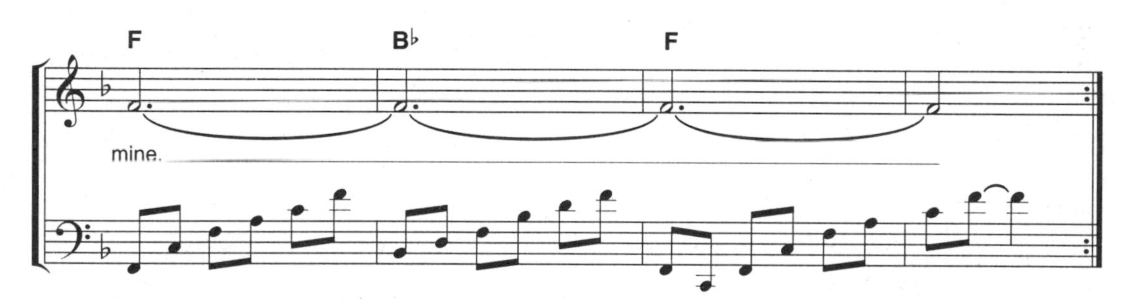

2.Sweet baby of mine in this stable so bare,
Entered this world to make us all care.
See how the animals will keep you warm,
They'll love you and lead you when men threaten harm.
And they will remember this moment in time,
Sweet baby of mine.

3.Sweet baby of mine, there are visitors here,
Brought by your signs from far and near.
Look how they worship you on bended knee,
A King in the manger they've come to see
And they will remember this moment in time,
Sweet baby of mine.

4.Sweet baby of mine, you bring joy to us all.
Cradled this night in the animals' stall.
The star shines above us with a radiant glow
The world will be watching as you grow and grow
But I will remember this moment in time,
Sweet baby of mine.

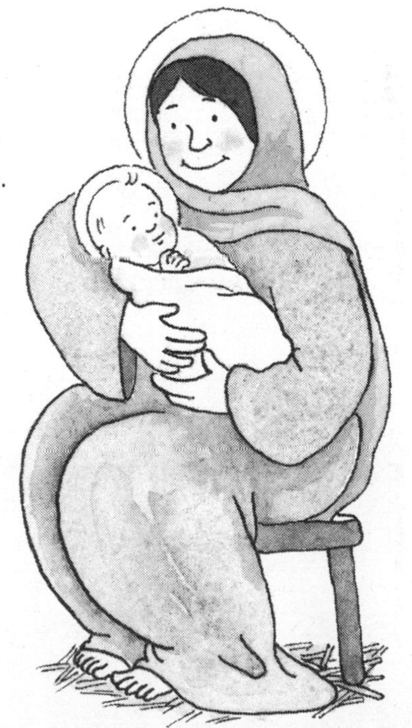

A star is shining

Clive Barnwell

Bm7 Gmaj7 Em7 A9 D Bm7
shin - ing o - ver jour - ney's end.
Gmaj7
1. Em7 A9 D D.%
Kings: 2. The even - ing
2. Em7 A9
G A D Bm7 F♯m
Both: And as I looked I saw that oth - ers saw it too.
D.C. to ⊕ then Coda
G A D Bm Em A
But they just shook their heads and car - ried on and ne - ver knew.
rit.
Coda D Bm7 Gmaj7 Em7 A9
A star is shin - ing o - ver jour - ney's end.
F♯m Bm Em G A
A star is shin - ing o - ver journ - ey's end.

Kings:
The evening air was cold and chill as I lay in my bed.
And though the palace gate was barred, I was awoken by the guard.
And as I woke I saw the star above the palace wall.
And I knew what I had to do. And even as I rode I knew.
A star is shining over journey's end.

Chorus

The evening air was cold and chill as I went on my way.
And to a stable I was led to see a babe in his straw bed.
And as I knelt before my Lord the world at once was bright.
And in the coldness of that stall began the story of them all.
A star is shining over journey's end.
A star is shining over journey's end.
And journey's end was where it all began.

Lullaby

Alan Simmons

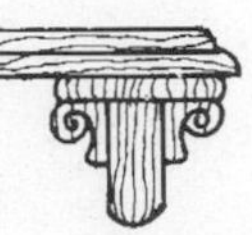

Welcome to the world

Debbie Campbell

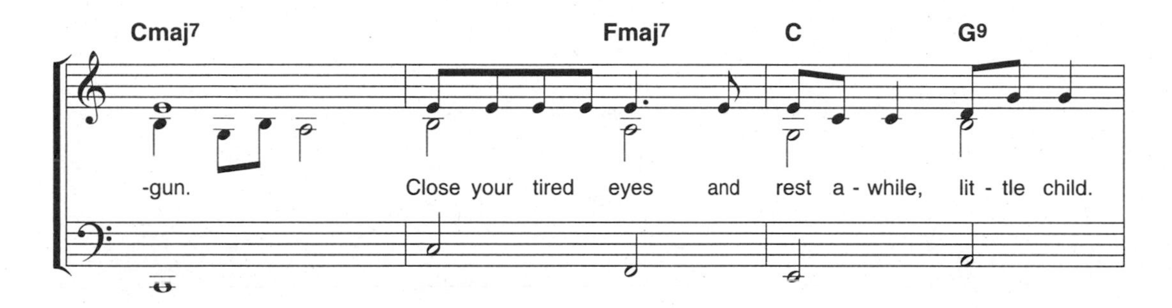

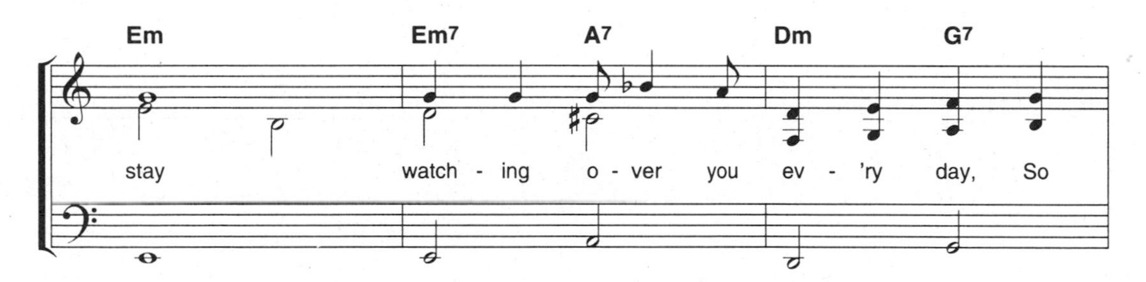

Child in the manger

Lesley Funge

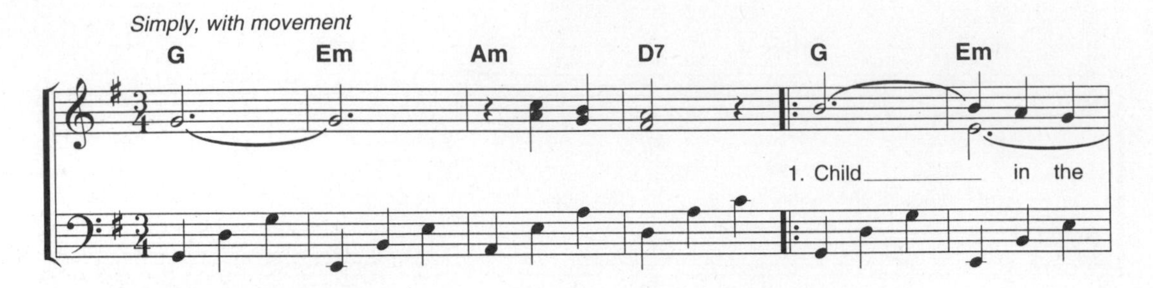

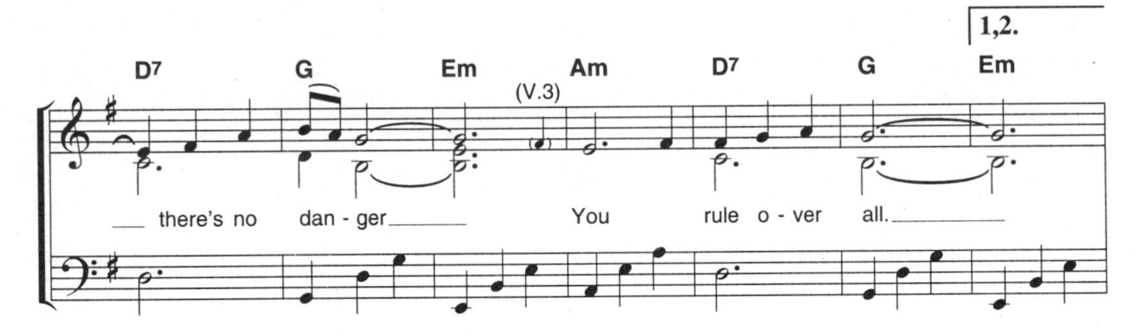

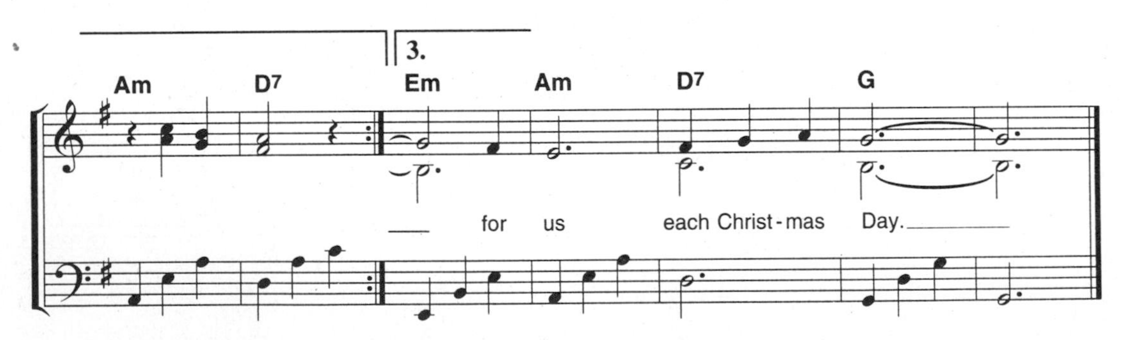

2.See – kings and shepherds, run – here to worship you;
See – how the beasts and birds, watch – over you too.

3.You – have come down to earth, here – in the hay,
We – celebrate your birth for us – each Christmas Day,
For us – each Christmas Day.

Whispering winds

Carole Henderson Begg

2.Whisper the story the shepherds told,
Of angel voices above the fold,
How they left their sheep the babe to find.
Whispering winds whisper on.

Chorus

3.Whisper the journey the wise men made,
Of the star they followed, and where they stayed,
Of the gifts they brought for Mary's son.
Whispering winds whisper on.

Chorus

We want to see what's goin' on!

Peter Morrell

2. We can't climb ladders or the steps,
It really isn't fair.
Why can't those people form a queue
Then we might have a better view?

All for the child

Clive Barnwell

2.So long ago and so far away.
Follow the star to where Jesus lay.
Gifts they are bringing.
Praises they're singing.
All for the child born upon Christmas day.

Follow that star

Clive Barnwell

2.Three wise men, far away, heard the voice as it grew.
They looked up, saw the light and so they followed too.

Chorus

Come shepherd, come

David Moses

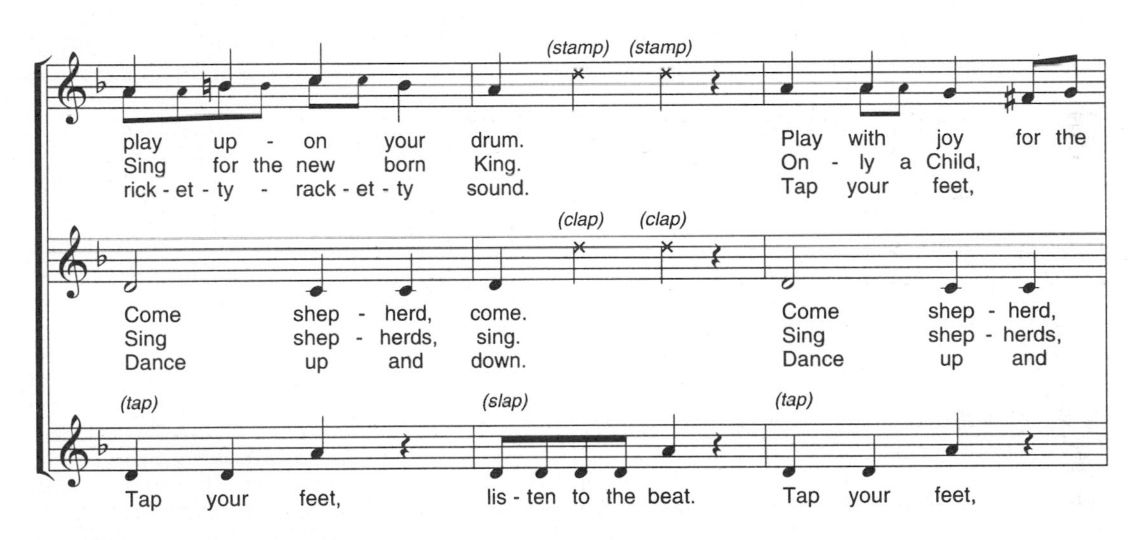

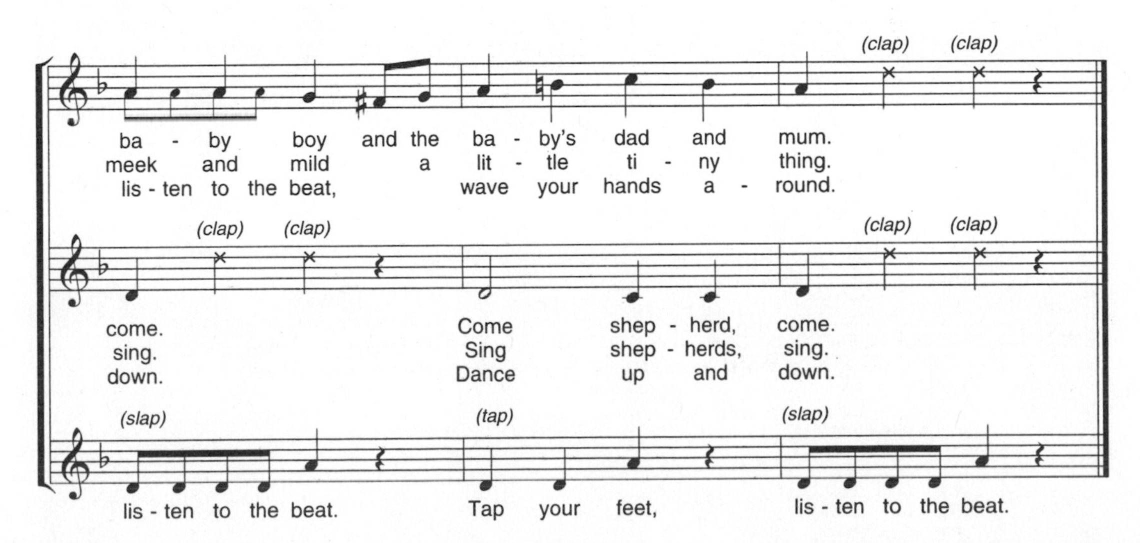

The brightest star

Lisa Mackenzie

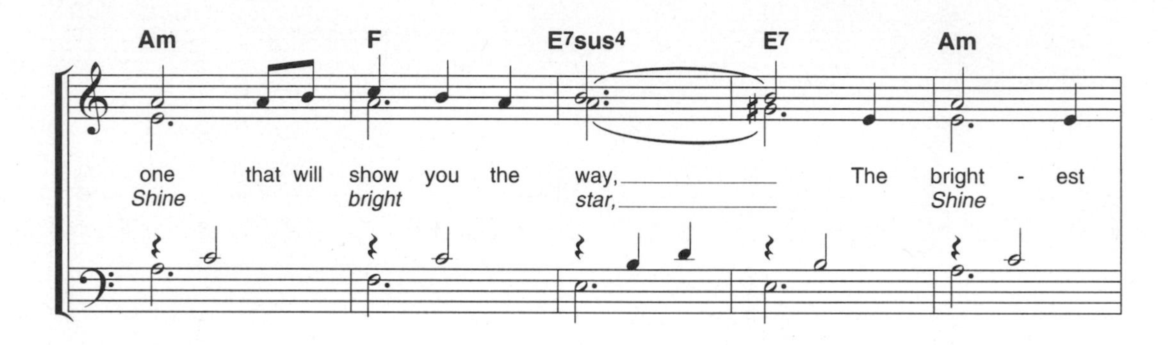

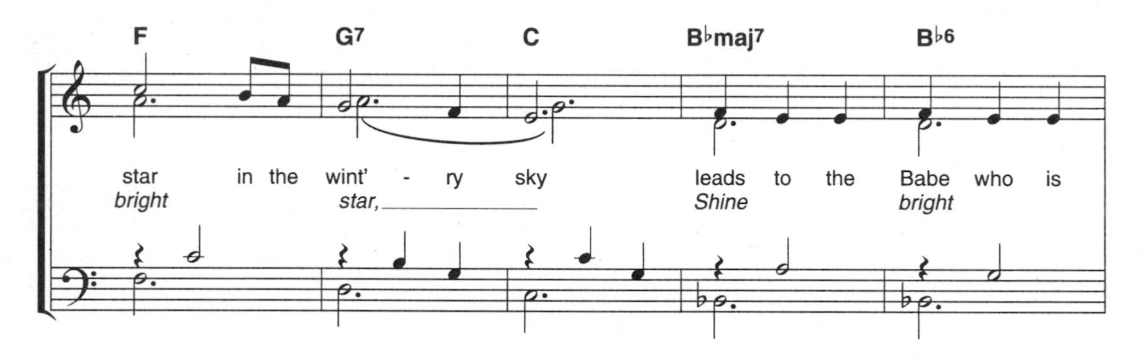

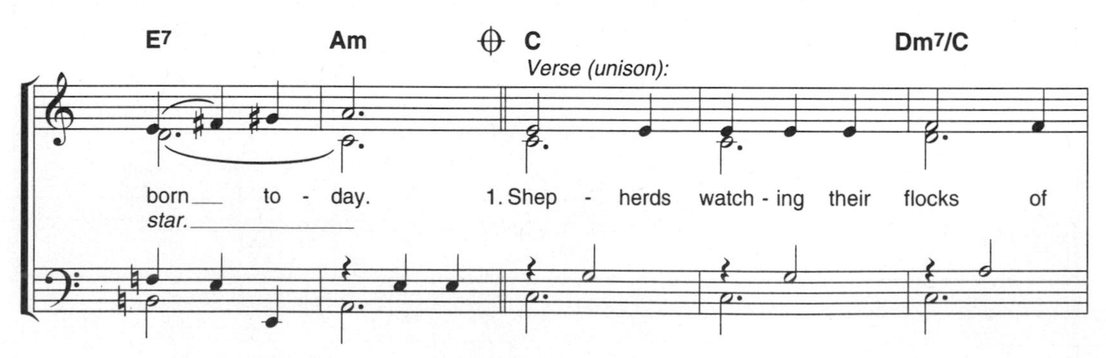

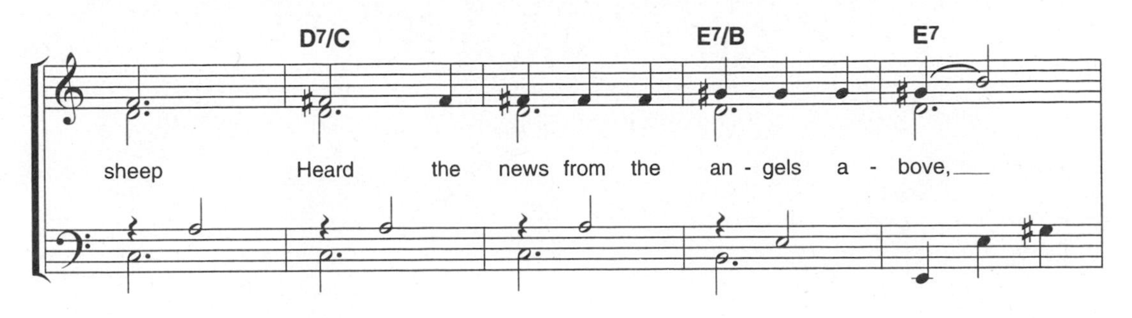

2.Three wise men from far Eastern lands,
Bearing gifts to that warm cattle stall,
Riding on camels o'er desert sands,
They started their search for the King of all.

Chorus

3.We can worship the newborn King,
Like the shepherds and kings of old.
With our hearts and voices we'll sing;
A gift for the Baby, more precious than gold.

Chorus

I wish I was a shepherd

Debbie Campbell

2.I wish I was a wise man on the day that Jesus was born.
I wish I was a wise man on that very first Christmas morn.
For if I was a wise man
I would follow a star up in the sky
To Jesus on the day that he was born.

3.I wish I was an angel on the day that Jesus was born.
I wish I was an angel on that very first Christmas morn.
For if I was an angel
I would sing a gentle lullaby
To Jesus on the day that he was born.

Three great kings

Lisa Mackenzie

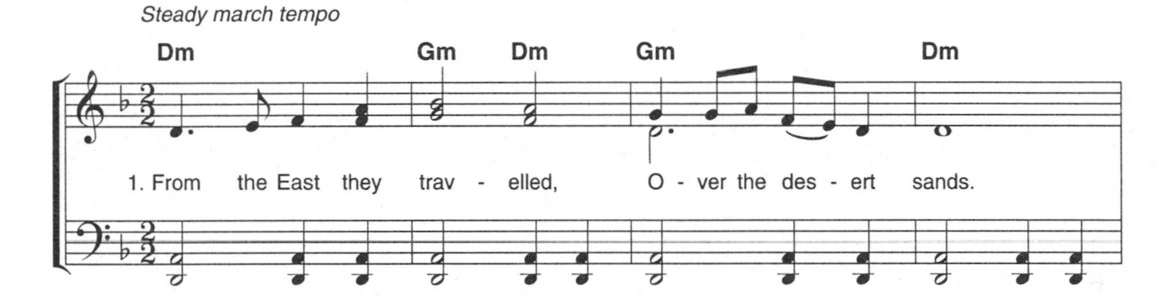

2.Gifts of frankincense and
Gold and myrrh they brought.
Stopped to ask directions,
Left Herod deep in thought.
While he planned his deadly deeds,
They followed the shining light.
Set on high to guide them
Through the wintry night.

3.Then at last they found Him,
In the stable bare.
Lying in a manger,
Mary and Joseph there.
So they laid their gifts before Him,
Three great kings were they,
Worshipping the baby,
Sleeping in the hay.

The following rhythm could be played on a hand drum throughout. These notes make an effective drone accompaniment, if played throughout on a xylophone, soft recorders or a violin.

Three wise men

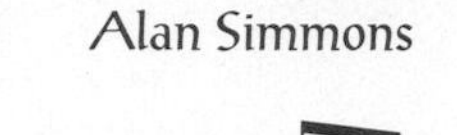

Alan Simmons

bring to crown Him a - gain.
-claim the birth, Joy - ful - ly sing!
earth that all man - kind may live.
(A) B♭
(E7) C7
(A) F

The stable door

Gillian Parker

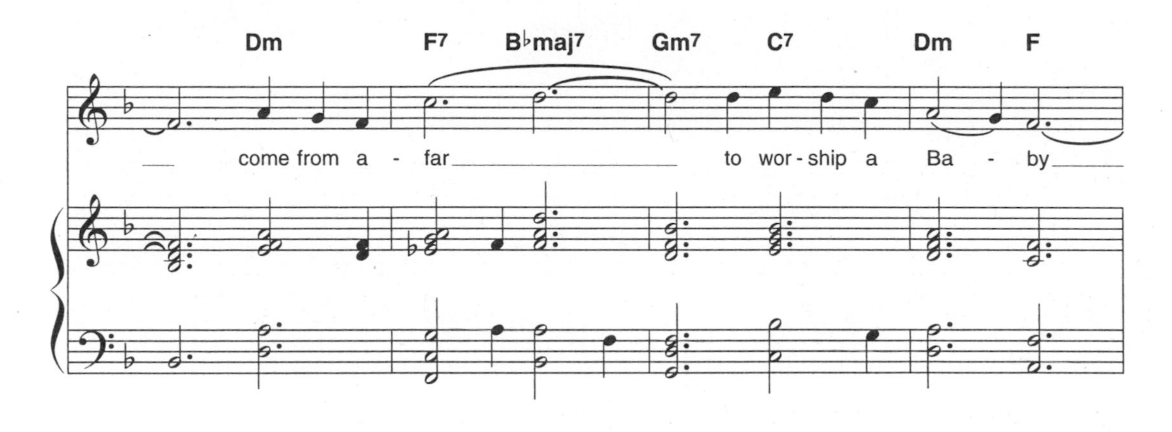

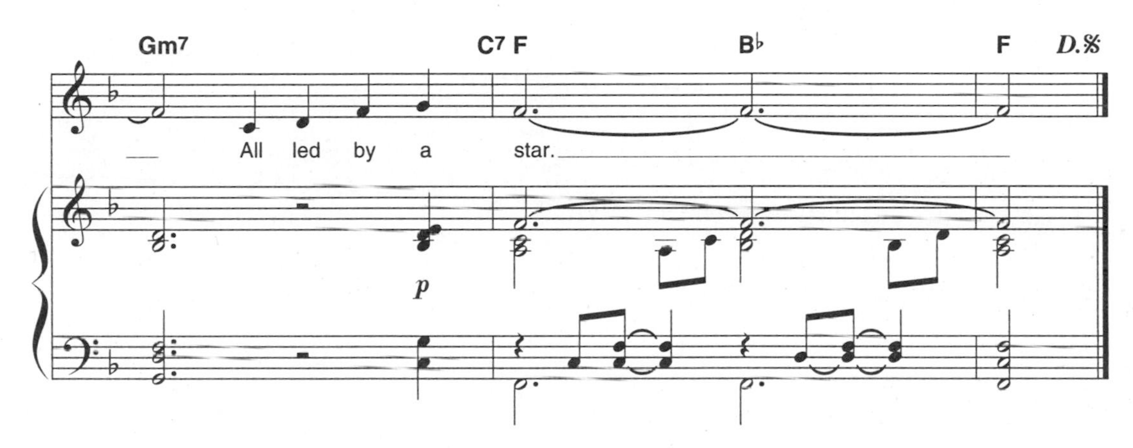

2.A maiden so simple
So young and so fair,
Who watched in surprise
At the gathering there –
Of oxen and asses,
Of shepherds and kings.
A sky filled with angels –
Their soft, beating wings.

3.And in that warm stable
Her baby was born.
A cry in the darkness
Of night before dawn.
His eyes watched her face
As it glowed with her love,
Then he slept while the star
Flickered brightly above.

4.I search through the sky
Once a year, on that night,
In case there's a star
Like that star, burning bright.
It makes me remember
What Christmas is for,
As I think of the stable
And open the door.

The golden star

Gerald Haigh

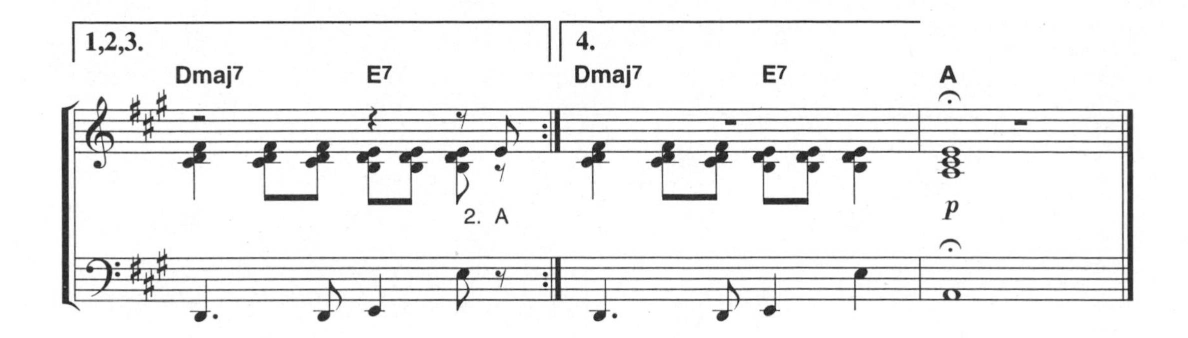

2.A hundred shuttered windows stand ajar
And curious faces peer.
The travellers set their course to where, afar
The golden star stands clear.

3.The steady footsteps fade towards the west
Out through the desert gates
Long miles ahead where child and mother rest
The golden star awaits.

4.So traveller, as you walk the darkling road
And lights dim one by one.
Look up, where once as Eastern princes showed
The golden star shines on.

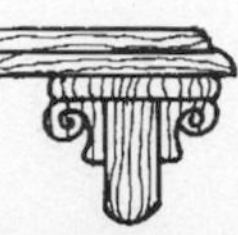

Rock a little baby

David Moses

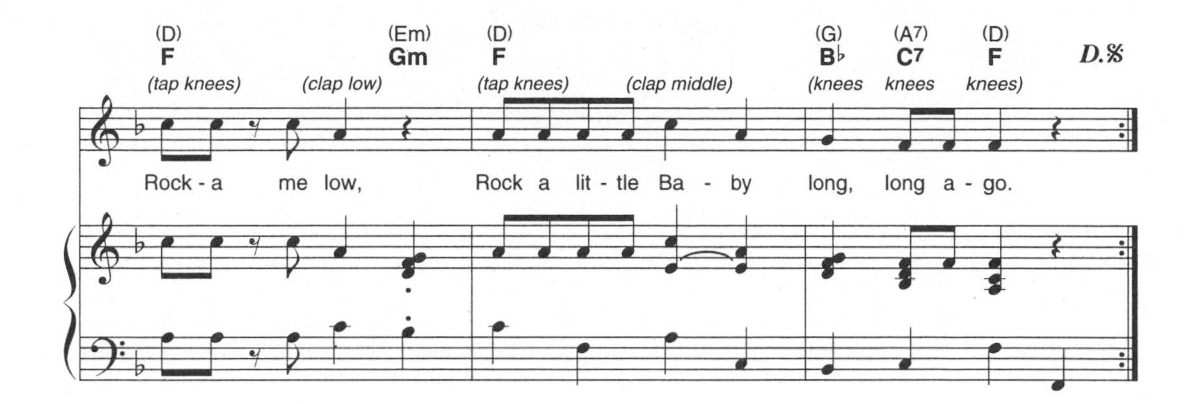

2.Did you ever hear of three wise men,
Came to a town called Bethlehem?

Chorus

3.Did you ever hear of a mother mild?
She gave birth to a holy child.

Chorus

4.Did you ever hear why the wise men came?
To see the child and bless his name.

Chorus

Baby Jesus, lying in a stall

Ian Henderson Begg

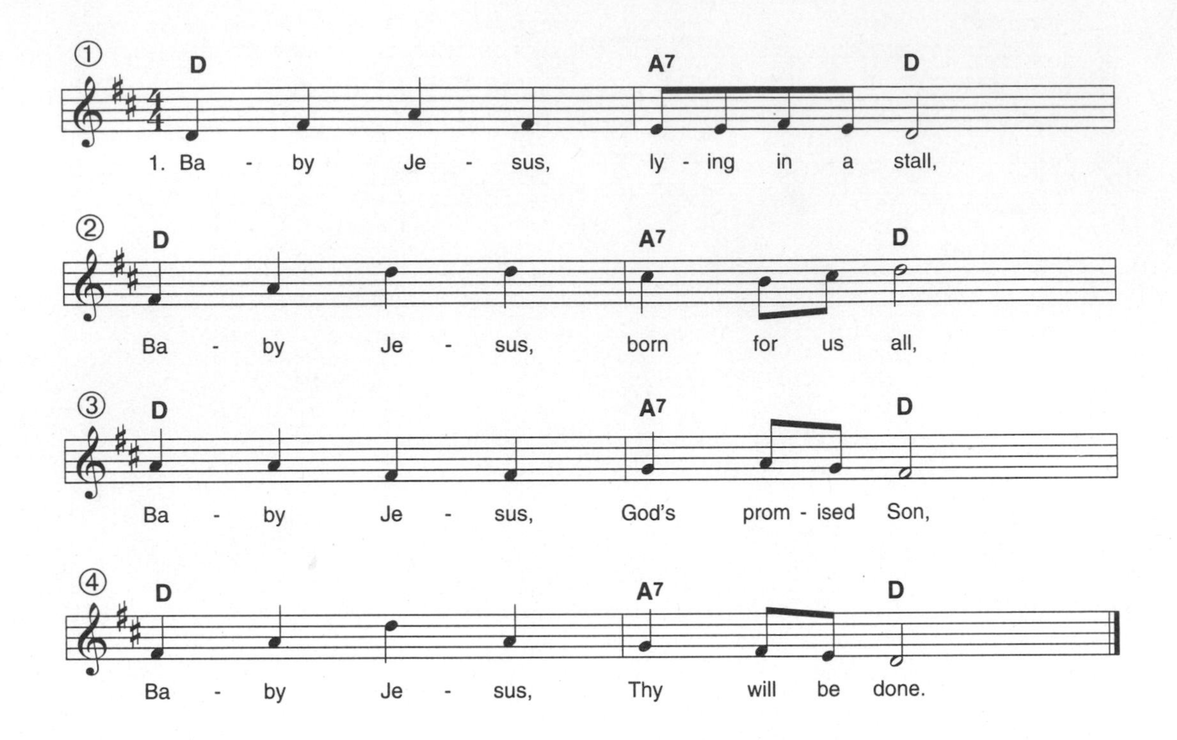

2.Born to Mary in Bethlehem,
Stable born, no room in the inn.
Shepherds came and wise men too,
Born a babe to save me and you.

3.Angels high in heaven above
Welcomed him, the Prince of Love.
All mankind may bow the knee
To the babe who set us free.

Repeat verse one

Note: this simple carol can be sung in three ways, straight as an ordinary carol, in canon, or with groups starting one line after the previous as a four-part round.

Hurry away

Ian Henderson Begg

2.Hurry away from Beth'lem,
Hurry off through the night,
Go and escape the soldiers,
They will come with the light.
Herod has heard the story
Heard what the wise men said;
He doesn't want to worship,
He wants you dead.

3.Hurry away, but quietly,
Rise up, be on your way.
Don't stop 'til you're in Egypt
You'll find a place to stay.
Once Herod's dead an angel
Will bring you news, you know.
Hurry away with Jesus,
It's time to go.

Coda:
Hurry away, Hurry away,
Hurry, hurry away. (*twice or more as desired*)

Bethlehem boy

Peter Morrell

D
G
He'll be a Beth - le - hem Boy, a
D
A7
D
D.C. first and second times
Beth - le - hem Boy, Born to help us all.
After Verse 3:
C
G
D7
f He was a Beth - le hem Boy, He was a heal - er, lead - er, teach - er, friend.
f
G
G7
C
G
He was a Beth - le - hem Boy, Al - ways

2.Mary and Joseph arrived to find
Nowhere to stay
Signs saying 'No Vacancies' were the
Rule of the day.
Joseph was offered a stable bed
Somewhere to lay.
Mary was thankful when Jesus was
Born in the hay.

Chorus:
He was a Bethlehem boy, a Bethlehem boy
Born in a cattle stall.
He was a Bethlehem boy, a Bethlehem boy
Born to help us all.

3.Jesus was born in a manger bed
Long, long ago
Born to be 'Light of the World', he had
Far, far to go.
Wise men and shepherds came from afar
On, on you go.
Follow the star shining bright to that
Town there below.

Chorus:
To see a Bethlehem boy, a Bethlehem boy
Born in a cattle stall,
To see a Bethlehem boy, a Bethlehem boy
Born to help us all.

He was a Bethlehem boy
He was a healer, leader, teacher, friend,
He was a Bethlehem boy
Always there to lend a helping hand.

4.His message goes on around the world
Peace, love and care
Our world exists for us all and we
Must learn to share.
So let us sing now at Christmas of
His gifts so rare
Jesus is with us all through our lives,
He's everywhere.

Chorus:
Yes, he's a Bethlehem boy, a Bethlehem boy
Born in a cattle stall
Yes, he's a Bethlehem boy, a Bethlehem boy
Born to help us, Heaven sent, yes, born to
help us all.

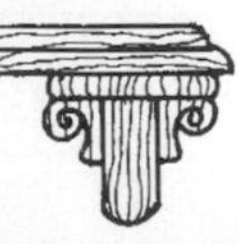

Christmas pictures in the fire

Ann Bryant

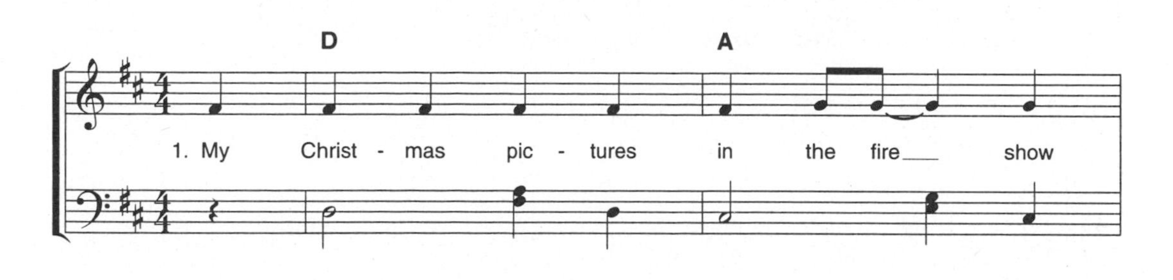

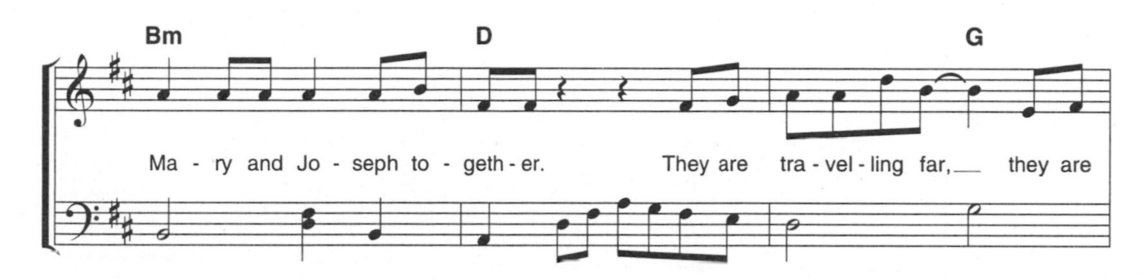

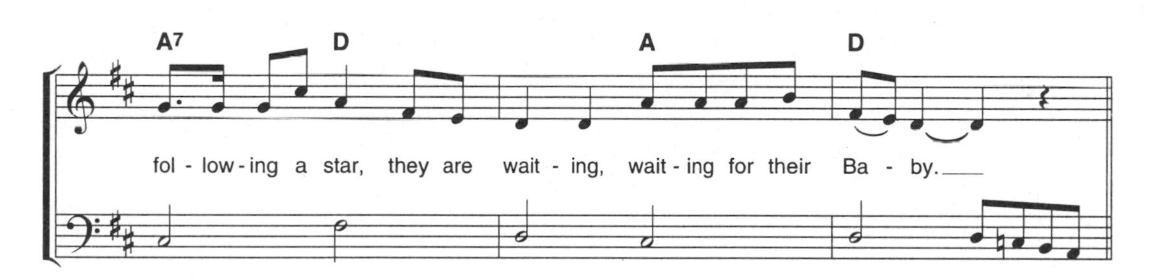

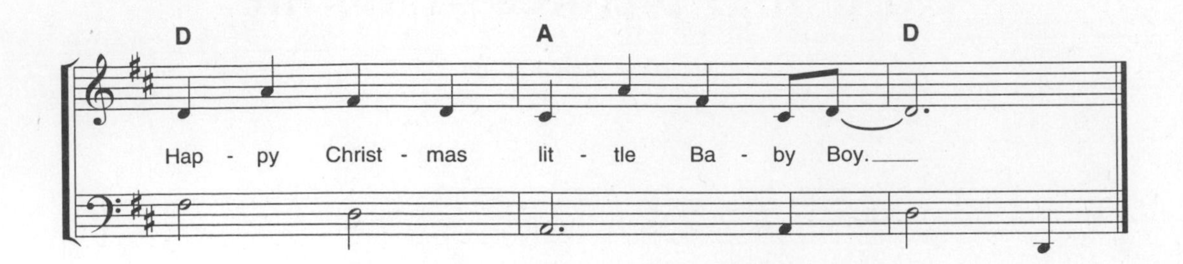

2.My Christmas pictures in the fire show animals talking in the stable.
They all cover their eyes as a voice from the skies
Says, 'You must go now to see the baby.'

Chorus

3.My Christmas pictures in the fire show shepherds going to the stable.
They all cover their eyes as a voice from the skies
Says, 'You must go now to see the baby.'

Chorus

4.My Christmas pictures in the fire show angels singing to the baby.
They are singing a prayer, it's for everyone there
In the stable visiting the baby.

Chorus

5.My Christmas pictures in the fire show wise men carrying their treasures.
They have journeyed for miles, just for one of his smiles.
He's a King and yet he's just a baby.

Chorus

6.My Christmas pictures in the fire show children dancing round the manger.
There is love, there is joy, for that sweet little boy.
He's a star child – King of all the babies.

Ring out those bells for him

Peter Morrell

2.Lived quite a humble life
Met with much toil and strife
Gained strength from God on high
Had a job to do.
Healing the sick and lame
Preaching about God's name
Teaching the living game
We can play it, so can you.

Chorus

3.Spent his life helping folk
Some without care or hope
Others would sit and mope
'Til he came along.
Then with his healing ways
Sick ones he'd gently raise.
People would sing his praise
Changing weak hearts into strong.

Chorus

O come and join the dance

Graham Kendrick

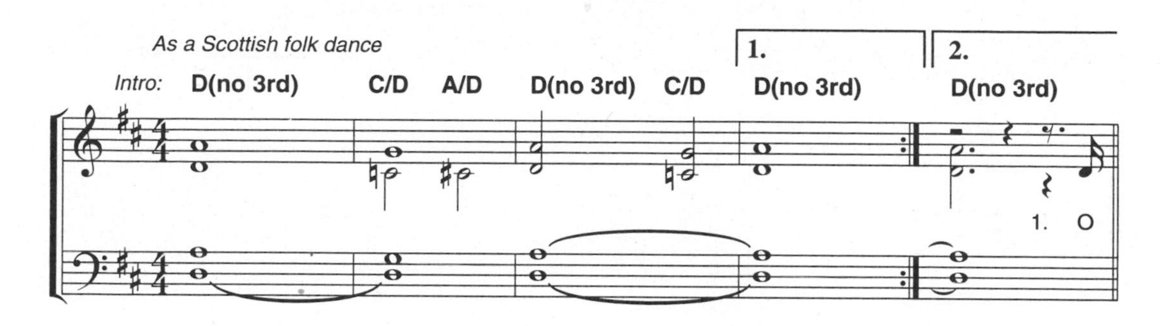

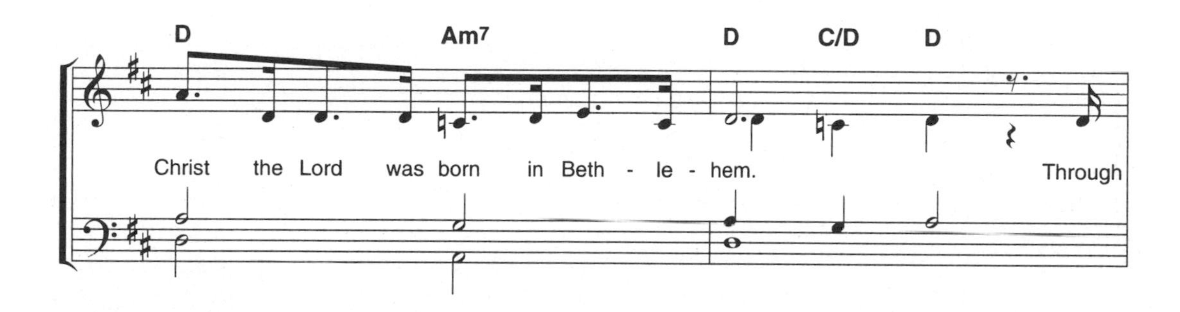

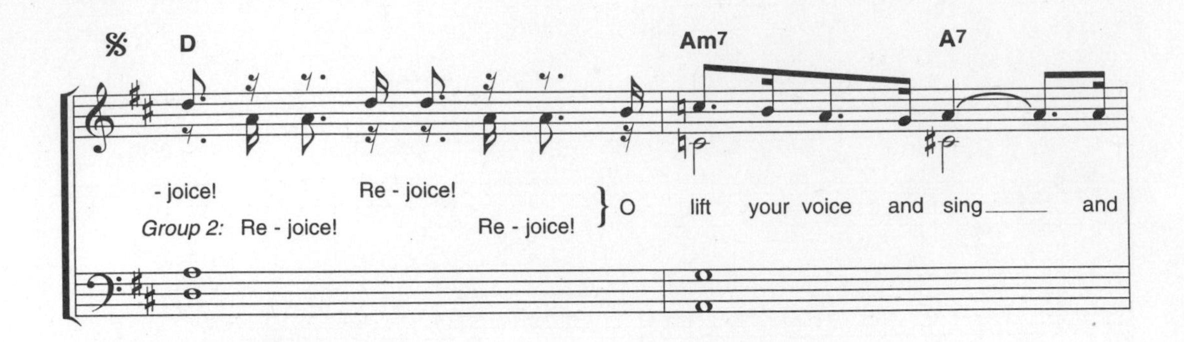
D
Am7
A7
- joice!
Re - joice!
Group 2: Re - joice!
Re - joice!
O lift your voice and sing and

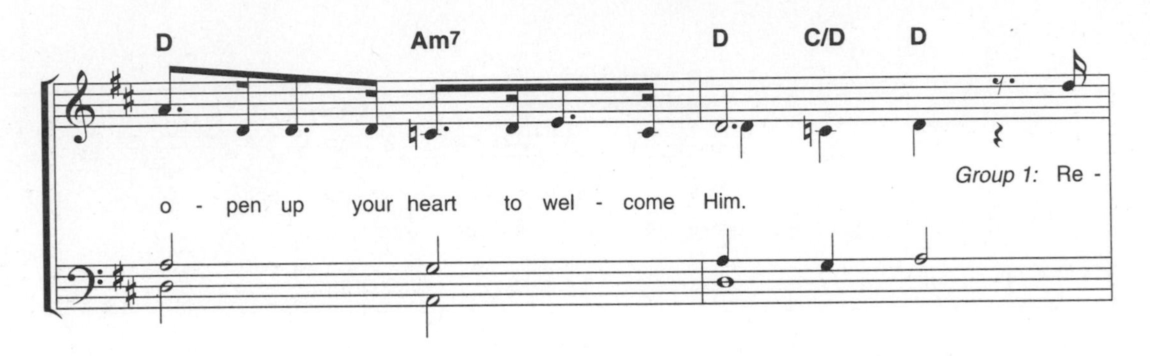
D
Am7
D C/D D
o - pen up your heart to wel - come Him.
Group 1: Re -

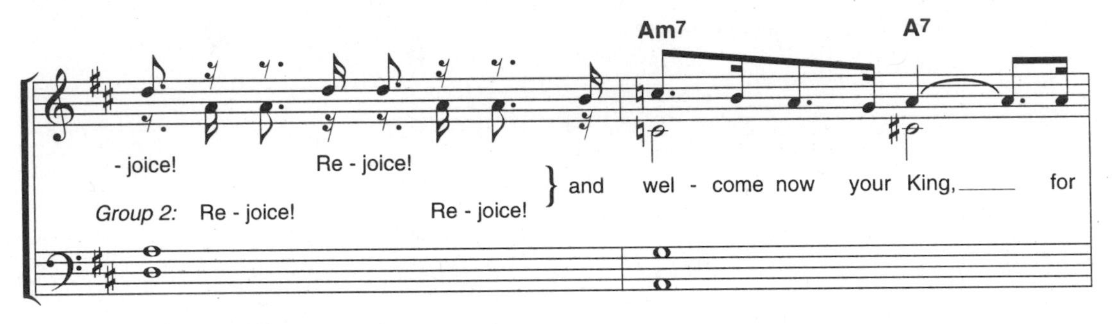
Am7
A7
- joice!
Re - joice!
Group 2: Re - joice!
Re - joice!
and wel - come now your King, for

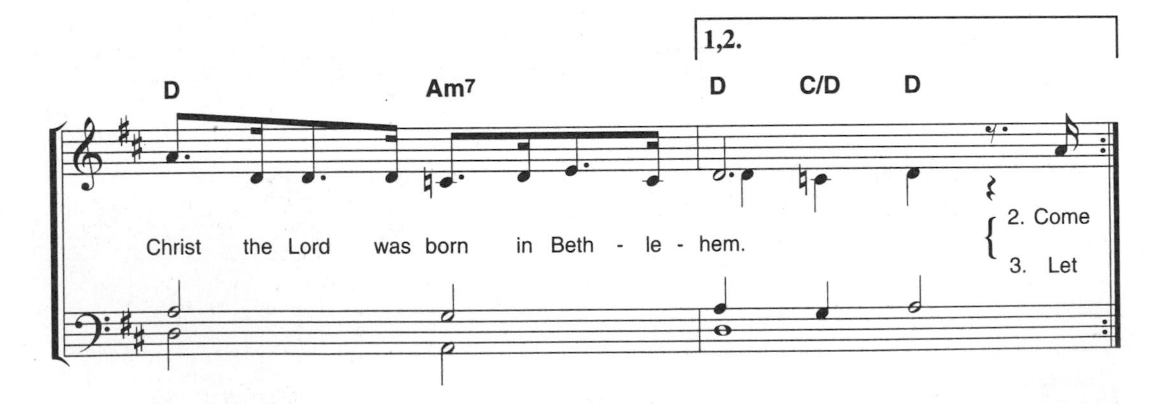
1,2.
D
Am7
D C/D D
Christ the Lord was born in Beth - le - hem.
2. Come
3. Let

(No more than one copy per child to be taken of this carol).

2.Come shed your heavy load
And dance your worries all away,
For Christ the Lord was born in Bethlehem.
He came to break the power of sin
And turn your night to day,
Oh, take my hand and come and join the song.

Chorus

3.Let laughter ring and angels sing
And joy be all around,
For Christ the Lord was born in Bethlehem.
And if you seek with all your heart
He surely can be found,
Oh, take my hand and come and join the song.

Chorus

A gift for a king

Ian Henderson Begg

2.If I could I would give him some food,
To make him feel good, and grow well;
But he needs just his mother's warm milk
And the comfort of her loving care.

Chorus

3.If I could I would give my best toy,
To keep him amused as he grows,
But a toy lasts for so little time
And he'll need other things in the end.

Chorus

4.So I'll sing him my own little song
That I've written especially for him.
And I'll sing with the love in my heart
That is due to my saviour and king.

Chorus

Jesus came that night

Jonathan Pudsey

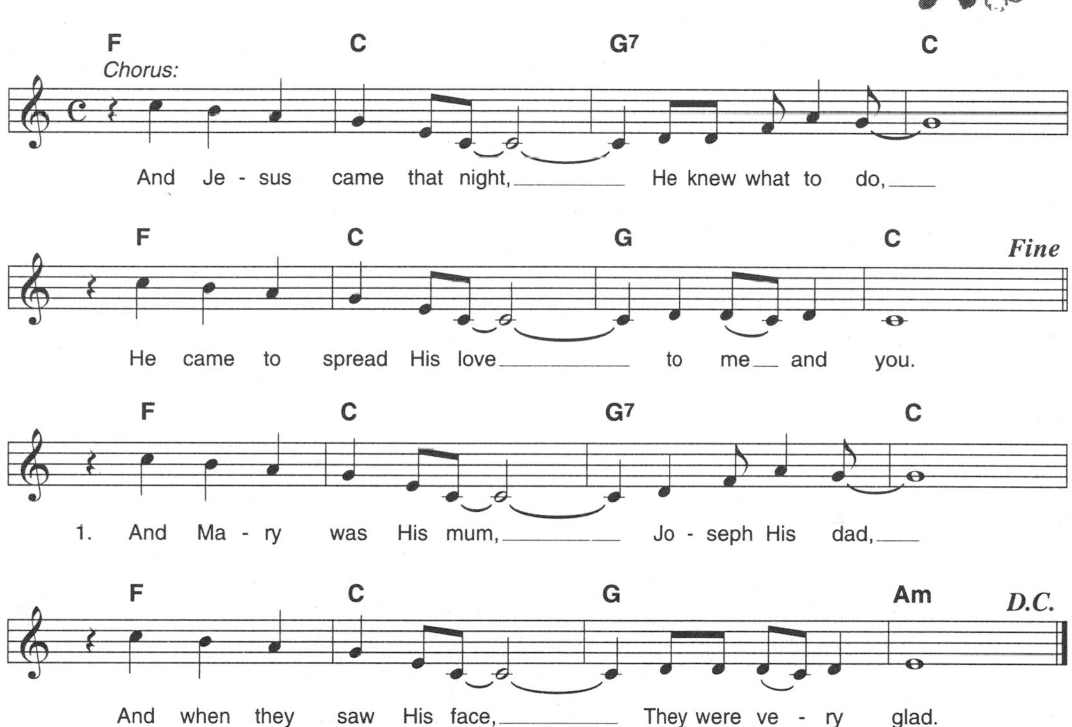

2. Some shepherds came to see
The new born King
And they bowed down and said,
'What a wonderful thing.'

Chorus

3. Three wise men came to see
The baby there,
They brought Him gifts of gold,
Frankincense and myrrh.

Chorus

The bells ring out

Gillian Parker

2. The bells ring out to children everywhere,
That Christmas Eve is here, there's magic in the air,
As eager tiny hands hang stockings up beneath the Christmas tree,
Hurry to bed then try to fall asleep.
Wondering what joys the early morning will bring,
Remembering the presents placed before the new born King,
And as they dream the night away, as did that baby long ago,
In His manger lay, with sweet smelling hay,
While His mother gently rocked Him in her arms.

Noel, Noel

Lonee Hewitt

Christmas time is here

Debbie Campbell

2.Celebrations with the family,
Friends and loved ones all join in.
Decorations on the Christmas tree
Let the festive time begin. Chorus

Starry nights

Lonee Hewitt

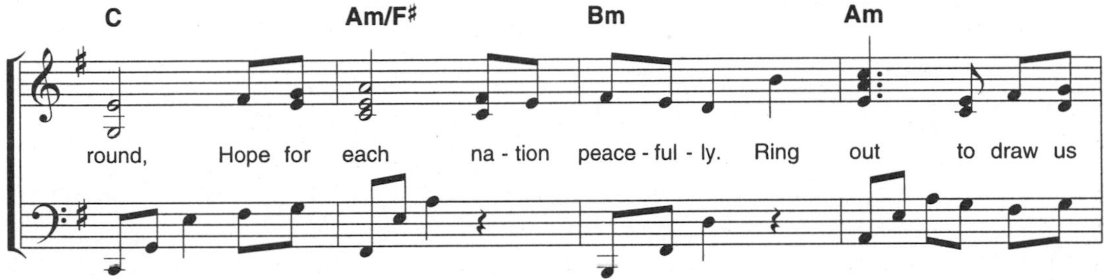

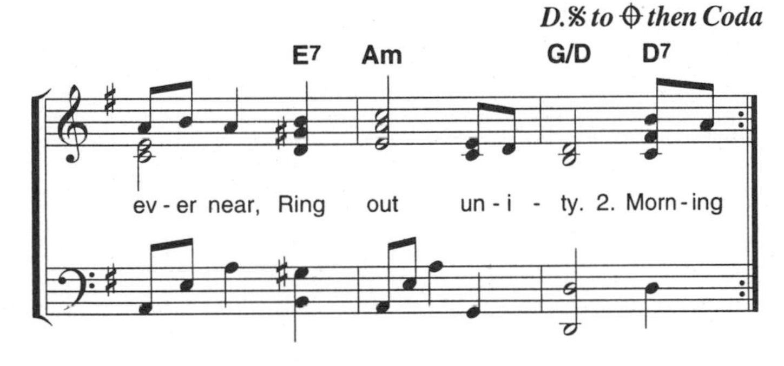

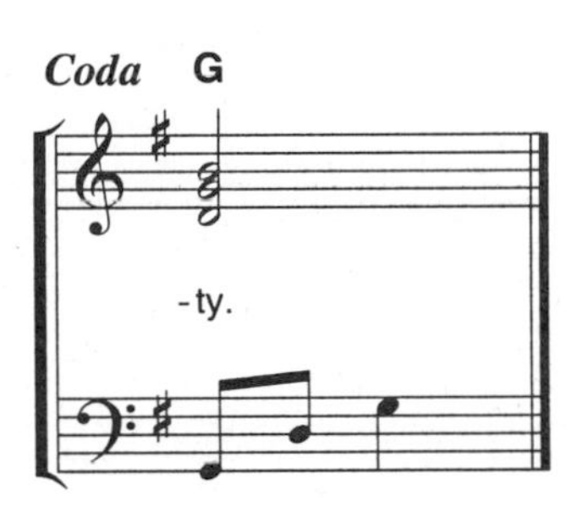

2.Morning star above the Holy Child,
Lead the way to peace on earth.
Ring the bells to sound a world of hope
Christ the King this day.
All should know this special time,
All should love and care.
To celebrate, to sing their songs of hope,
Give peace its name.
At this time of joyous praises
People love and share.
At this time thought for all
And there are eyes that care.
So let the message echo round,
Hope for each nation peacefully.
Ring out to draw us ever near,
Ring out unity.

3.Morning star above the Holy Child,
Lead the way to peace on earth.
Ring the bells to sound a world of hope
Ring out unity.

One little thing

Ann Bryant

2.Did you touch the baby's hand? Did he feel like a king?
He was just like a child but for one little thing,
When he held my frozen hand which was wrinkled and old
He brought life to my fingers and melted my cold.

Chorus

3.Did you hear the little boy? Did he sound like a king?
He was just like a child but for one little thing,
When the animals awoke and they lowed and they brayed
He just lay there and smiled at the noises they made.

Chorus

4.Do you have to live in fear? Do you have to make war?
If you only had seen all the love that I saw.
Build a castle in the air, dream a dream, cast a spell,
Wrap a coin in a prayer for our world's wishing well.

Chorus

If they give me peace for Christmas

Clive Barnwell

2.Though I like the Christmas tree,
Fairy dolls are not for me.
Writing cards out extra neat
Is not my favourite Christmas treat.
What I'd like is peace for Christmas this year.

3.Still I love most Christmas things,
All the good times that it brings.
But it could be better still,
And one day soon perhaps it will.
If they give me peace for Christmas this year.

The real Christmas message

Lisa Mackenzie

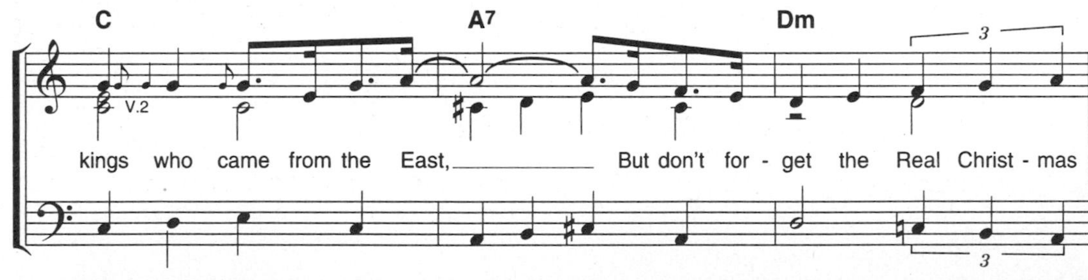

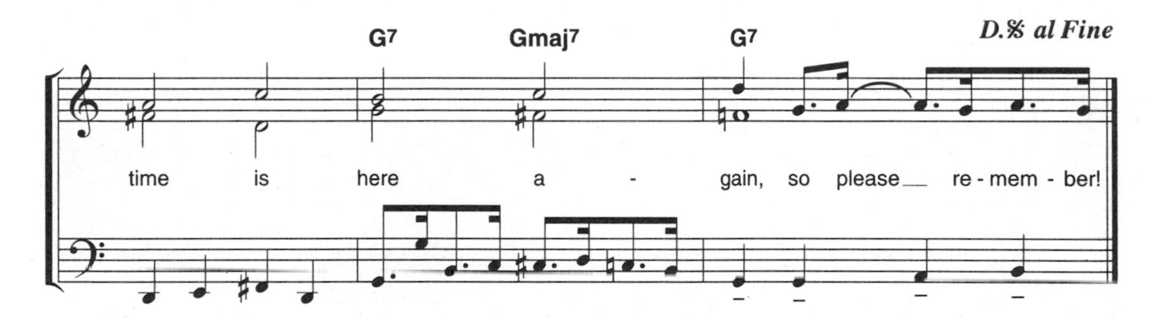

2. We all know about the shining star,
And Mary and Joseph who had travelled far,
We know about the stable and the manger,
And the donkey, that tired old beast,
But don't forget the Real Christmas Message
Of Love and Peace.

Chorus:
Peace on earth, goodwill to men,
Christmas time is here again.
So please remember!

3. We all know about this troubled world,
And children less fortunate than you and me.
We know about the battles and the famine,
Hope and pray one day they will cease,
So don't forget the Real Christmas Message
Of Love and Peace. (Yeah!)

The Christmas Child

Graham Kendrick

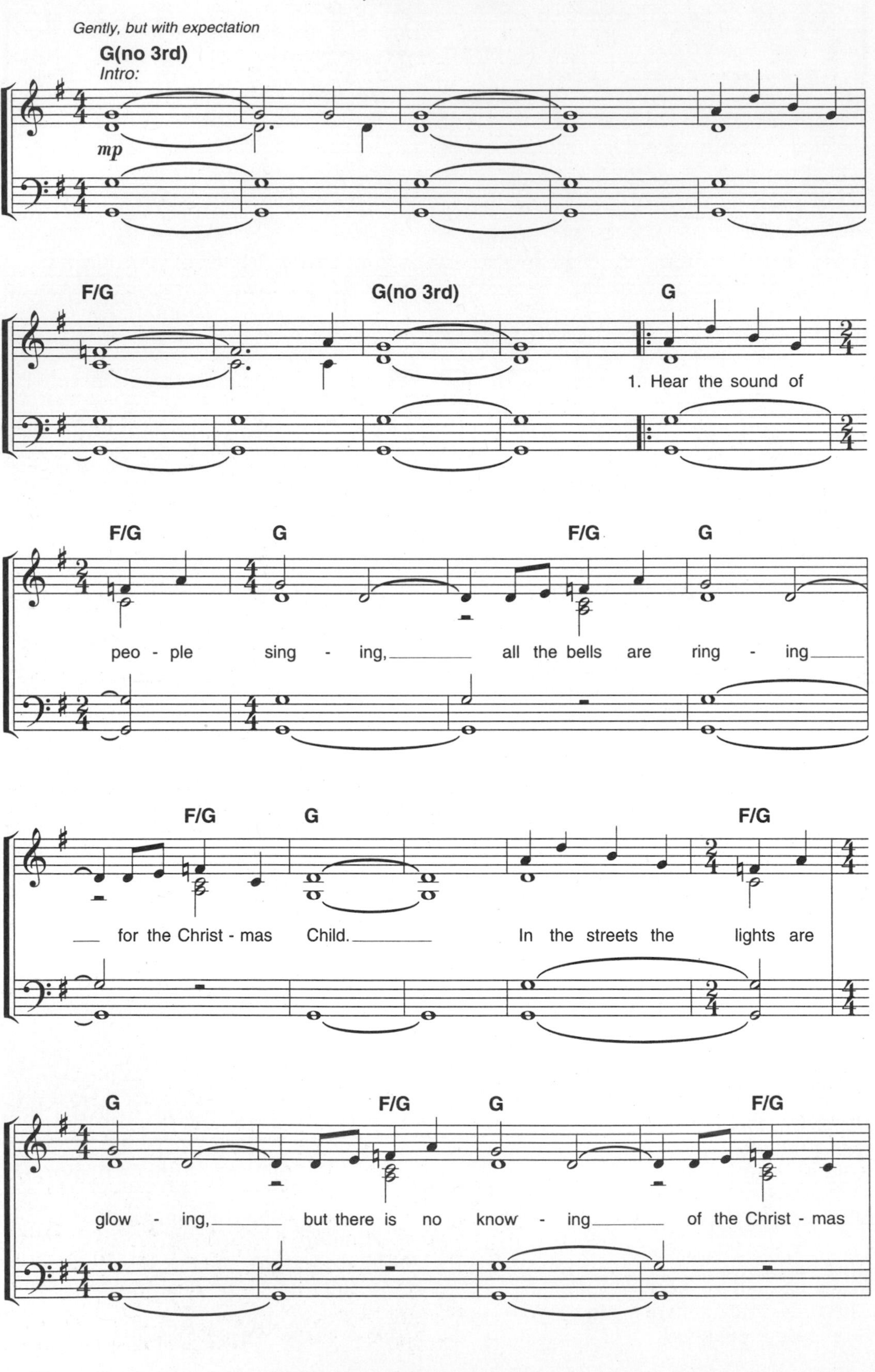

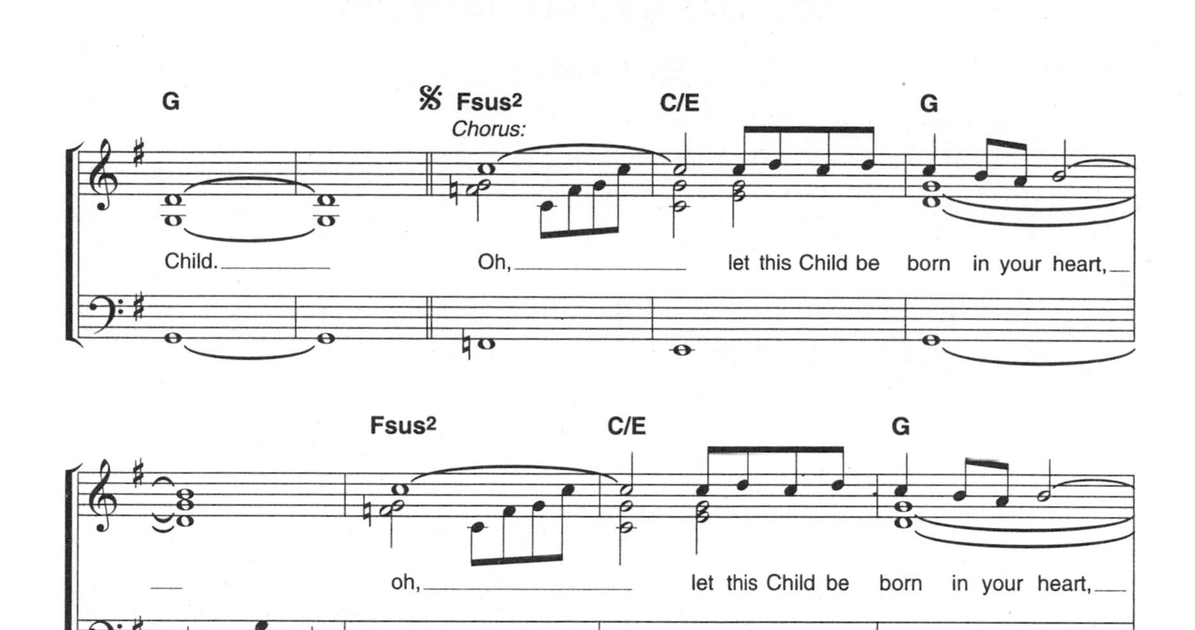

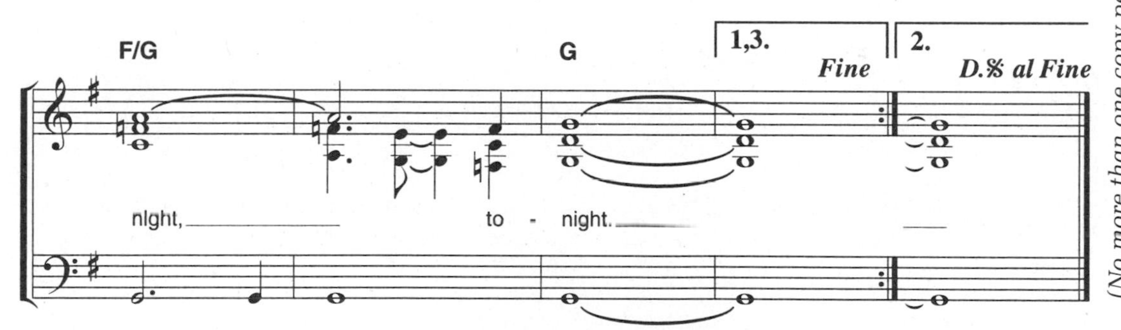

2.Will our wars go on forever,
And will peace be never
At Christmas time?
If we keep Him in the manger
Then there is no danger
From the Christmas Child.

Flavour of Christmas

Clive Barnwell

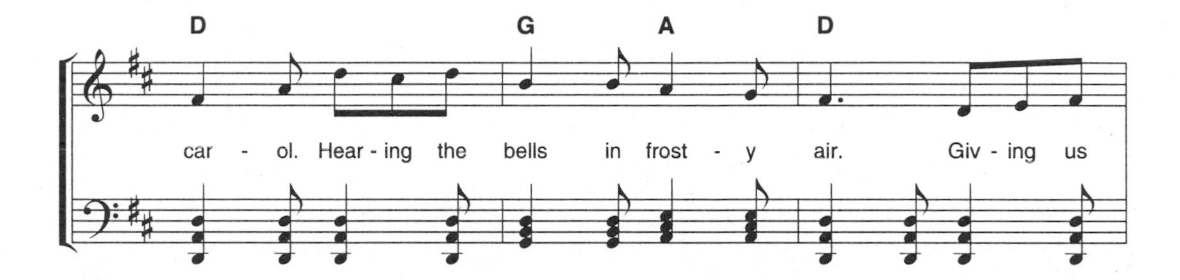

2.Smell the turkey
And cut the pudding
And find the sixpence
That's hidden within.
Through the window
The snow is falling
And Christmas has
Truly come in.

Chorus

Christmas ringers

Ian Henderson Begg

2.May your chimes renew our gladness,
Fill our hearts with joy and love.
Let the sound remind its hearers
Of the child sent from above. Chorus

3.May your ringing on that morning
Tell the message loud and clear,
Christmas celebrates the baby
Who our sins was born to bear. Chorus

4.Born an infant in a stable,
Yet His was the destiny
On the cross to die, yet blameless,
Die to set us sinners free. Chorus

5.So may you, with your clear ringing,
Pierce the hearts of everyone.
Christmas may be fun and presents,
But it celebrates God's Son. Chorus

Try an autoharp to accompany this carol.

The greatest story

Lisa Mackenzie

2.Holly leaves and ivy are evergreen,
Just like the greatest love the world has seen,
Jesus in the manger through His lowly birth,
Brought the love of God to everyone on earth.

Chorus

3.Share a festive meal with your family,
Sing happy carols round the Christmas tree.
Jolly old traditions loved by young and old,
Celebrate the greatest story ever told.

Chorus

Starlight

Clive Barnwell

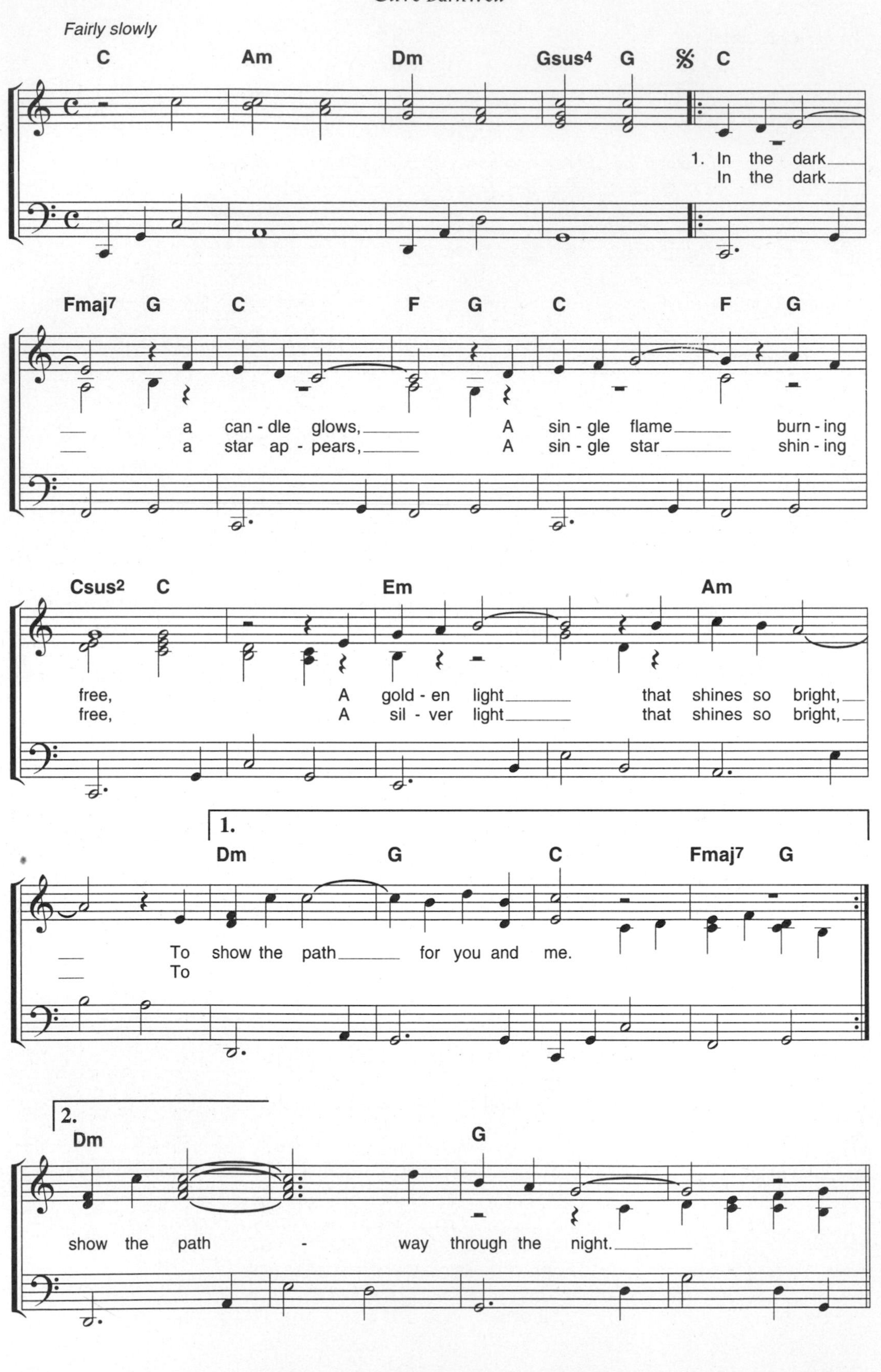

2.In the dark a glow appears,
A special glow no-one can see.
It warms the night. It reaches out
And touches you and touches me.

From the dark the sun appears,
A brighter day begins to grow.
There won't be dark like dark before
The light will shine for ever more.

Chorus

If I'd been born in Bethlehem

Lesley Funge

2.If I'd been born in Bethlehem so many years ago
I might have seen that star so bright, a star for the shepherds to know.
A star so bright, that glorious night, I might have seen it glow –
If I'd been born in Bethlehem so many years ago.

3.If I'd been born in Bethlehem so many years ago,
I might have smelt the fresh sweet hay and the animals jostling to and fro,
The ox, the ass, the donkey too, I might have heard them bray and low,
If I'd been born in Bethlehem so many years ago.

4.If I'd been born in Bethlehem so many years ago,
I might have tasted the bitter myrrh of the wise men bending low.
Their gifts they bring, fit for a king, but how could a child be so?
A child be a king in Bethlehem so many years ago?

5.If I'd been born in Bethlehem, so many years ago,
I might have felt in that stable bare the greatness that the whole world should know,
A king, a king, let church bells ring, set all the world aglow
With love that came down to Bethlehem so many years ago.

The candle song

Graham Kendrick

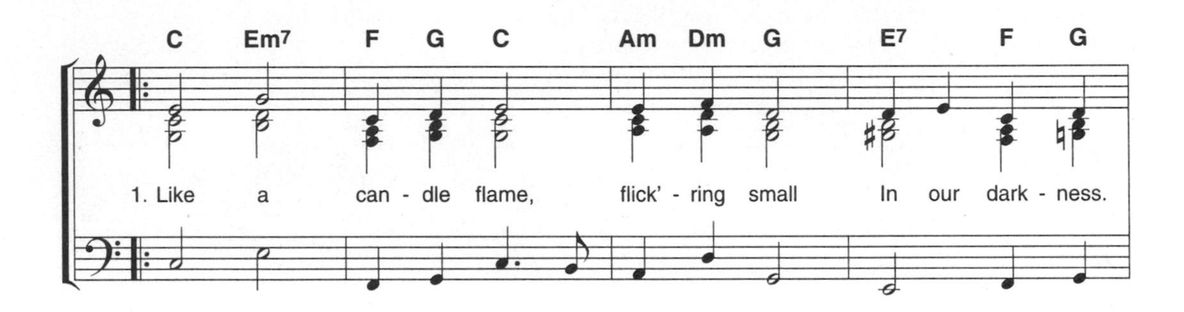

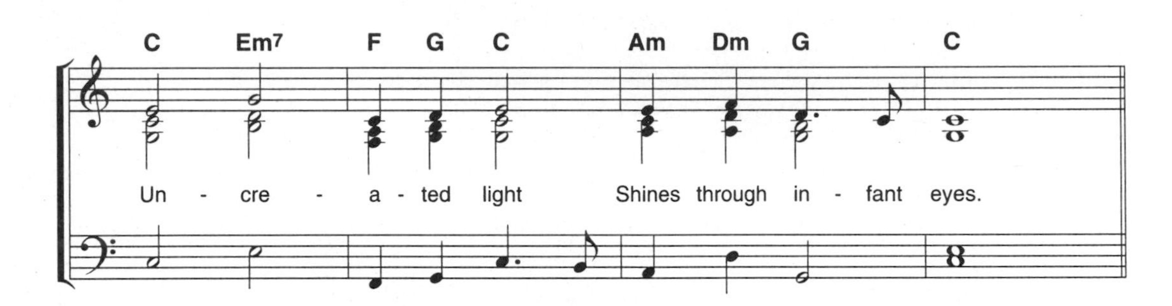

2.Stars and angels sing,
Yet the earth
Sleeps in shadows;
Can this tiny spark
Set a world on fire?

3.Yet His light shall shine
From our lives,
Spirit blazing,
As we touch the flame
Of His holy fire.

The message

Clive Barnwell

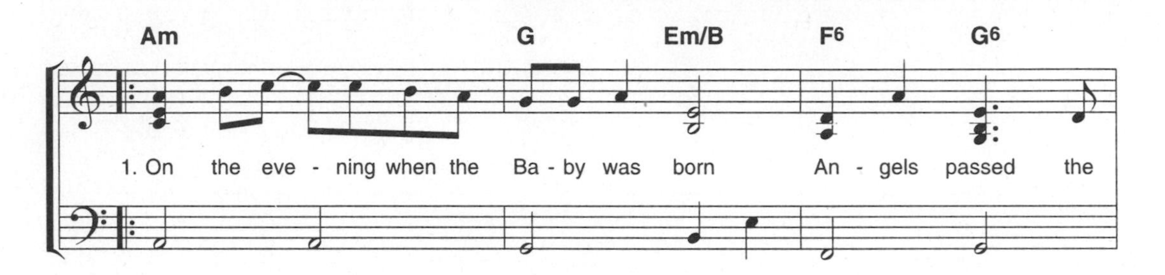

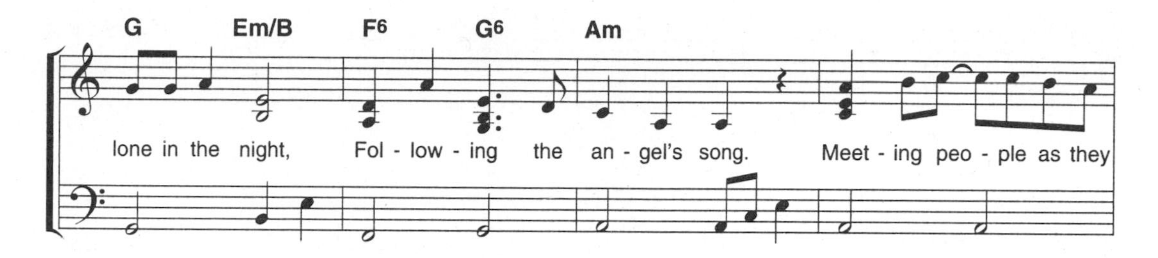

2.All the people that the shepherds had told
Went and passed the message on.
Love and happiness has come to the world,
Peace on earth for ev'ryone.
As it passed through the land
Others heard the story
Told by travellers in distant lands
All about the glory,
Spreading further 'til it covered the earth
Stories of the Father's Son.
Many years beyond the miracle birth,
Still the message carried on.

3.Though it happened long ago in the past
Still we pass the message on.
Love and happiness has come to the world,
Peace on earth for ev'ryone.
As we sing out our song
Let the whole world hear us.
Still the message travels loud and strong;
It's the word of Christmas.
What the future brings you never can tell,
But that's where we all belong.
Like the shepherds as we travel the road
We will pass the message on.

Stars shine bright

Peter Morrell

2.As He grew, the Christ child showed
Man a way to live.
Helped the poor and healed the sick,
Gave all He could ever give.
Left this Earth to save us all
To lift us up each time we fall.
Now we need Him by our side
His message then will be our guide.

Chorus

You came from the highest

Graham Kendrick

Em7
D
Em
D
Em
Cmaj7
Hea - ven's ex - alt - ed King,
Home - less and poor in Beth - le -
D
Chorus:
G
D
hem.
And we will sing Your song,
Am7
Em7
D
D/C
Am7
Fol - low You, for e - ver.
We will be Your hands
Em7
D
G
D
Reach - ing out a - gain.
Your song goes on and on,
Your
Am7
Em7
D
D/C
Am7
laugh - ter breaks the si - lence.
The sea - son of Your joy
Will

2.You came from the kindest,
To suffer the cruelest,
You are the message of love.
You came from the purest,
To die for the foulest,
You are the message of love.
Our God unrecognised,
For ruined sinners crucified.

3.In the bustle of main street,
The noise and the concrete,
Make us Your message of love.
In the turmoil of nations,
Or a heart's desperation,
Make us Your message of love.
Each step, each breath we take,
Yours is the love we celebrate.

So long ago

Ann Bryant

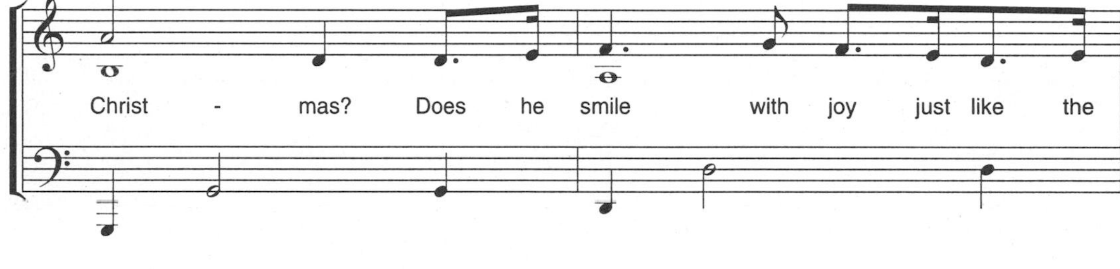

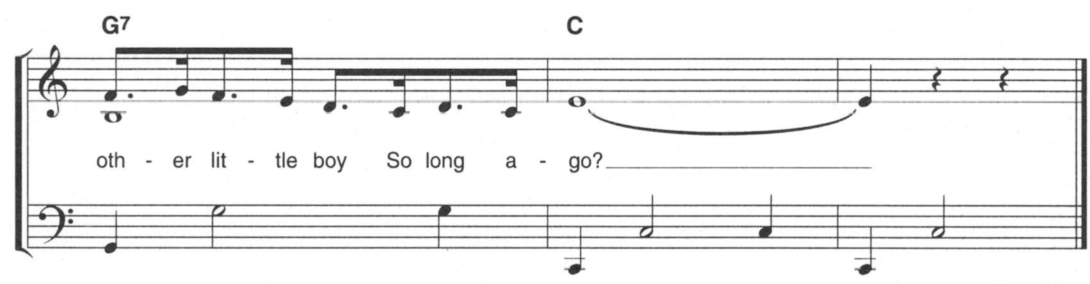

2.See a donkey in a field.
Do you think of Christmas?
Does he softly bray
Because he knows about the day
So long ago?

3.See a star up in the sky.
Do you think of Christmas?
Is it silver bright just
Like the star that filled the night
So long ago?

4.On an ordinary day
Do you think of Christmas?
Does the sky above
Fill the world with peace and love
From long ago?

Joyeux Noel

Richard Llewellyn

C♯m7 F♯m B7
Cov - ered in white, Now the Light of the
E A E B7 E D.𝄋 to ⊕ then to Coda
World is here to burn so bright.
Coda E B7 C♯m7
Christ - mas is here, Ring
Je - sus is here, Go
F♯m7 B7
out the bells. Glor - y to Man -
forth and tell, Glor - y to the
E A E B7 E
kind this day, Joy - eux No - el.
Lord this day, Joy - eux No - el.

Sing joy

Lonee Hewitt

2.All peoples of the world
All nations, join with us to say
Speak as one – live in peace –
All to love – at Christmas time.

Christmas is the time...

Jane Morgan

Try further verses by substituting appropriate words such as Jesus, sharing, caring, loving, laughing, where the word 'giving' occurs.

CHRISTMAS AROUND THE WORLD

Christmas down in the market square

Ian Henderson Begg

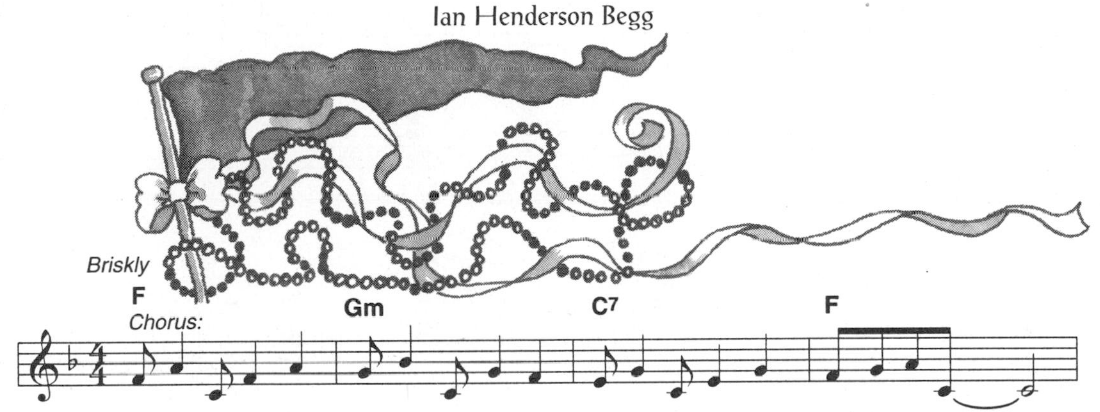

2.Ev'rybody's dressed in bright coloured clothes with
Ribbons and beads they look very fine.
What a Christmas party ev'ryone's having,
Dancing and singing in the Square. Chorus

3.Nobody is working on Christmas morning,
Ev'ryone's laughing, singing along.
Can't you feel the magic of the occasion
Christmas Day in the Market Square? Chorus

Heaven on earth

Peter Morrell

2.We've come to Bethlehem
To see the newly-born King
And we all hope, that He will cope
With the problems ahead. Chorus

3. We've brought You special gifts
From different places in time;
These we now give, and they come with
Love from us to the child. Chorus

4.Now we must leave this scene
And go back to our own time.
As we leave here, He is so near,
Can't we take Him back home? Chorus

Through the technology of the future, children are able to travel back to Bethlehem to see the new-born King. They come from different places in the world and different times in history.

Christmas around the world

Lesley Funge

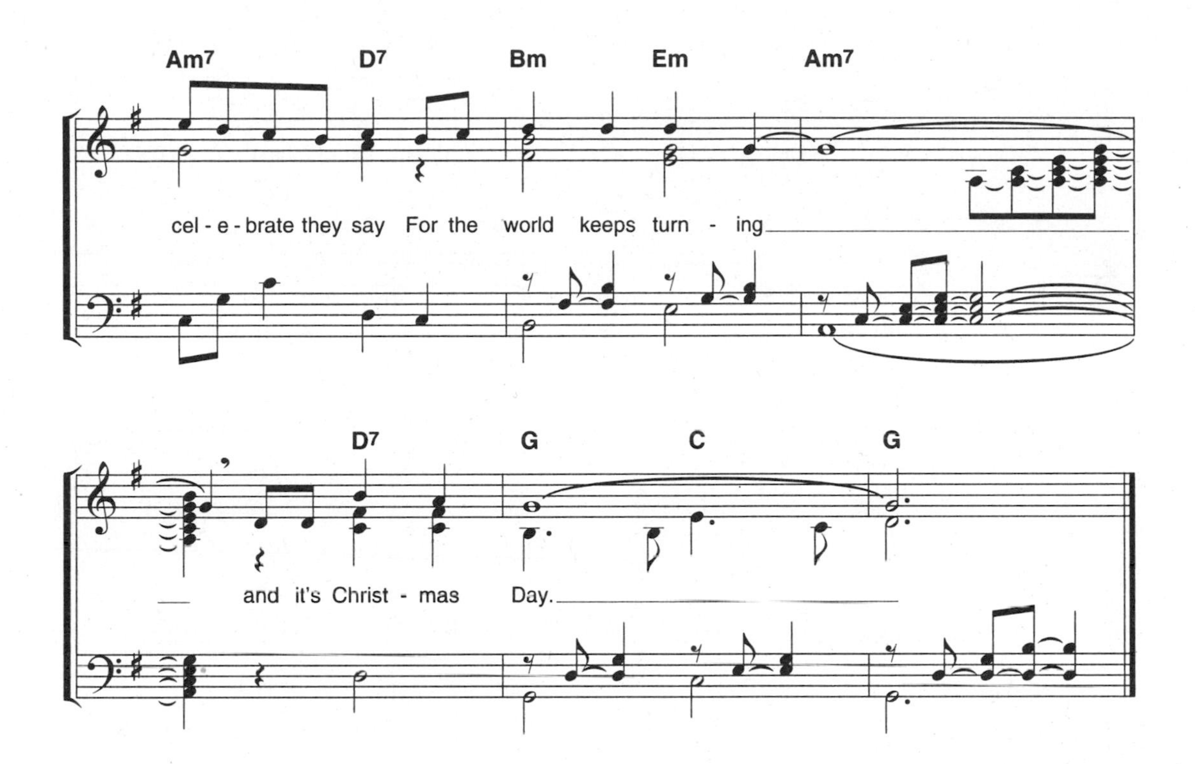

2.In the vast, vast plains of Australia
Where the Southern Cross doth shine,
And a Christmas treat is a 'barbie' on the beach,
Leave the winter's snow behind.
Yes it's Christmas, full of joy and fun,
Yes it's Christmas in the heat and in the sun,
Yes it's Christmas, celebrate they say
For the world keeps turning and it's Christmas Day.

3.In the far, far East in the desert heat
Where the wise men travelled a-while,
They were led to a stall by the brightest star of all
And they worshipped the Holy Child.
It was Christmas, they gave their gifts with joy,
The First Christmas, to a very special boy.
It was Christmas, celebrate they say
For the world keeps turning and it's Christmas Day.

4.In the giant continent of the West
There is every colour and clime,
And the people's mirth celebrates a baby's birth
And God's love for all mankind,
Yes it's Christmas, ring it loud and clear,
Yes it's Christmas, let the whole world hear
That it's Christmas, celebrate they say
For the world keeps turning and it's Christmas Day.

Christmas on the beach

Ian Henderson Begg

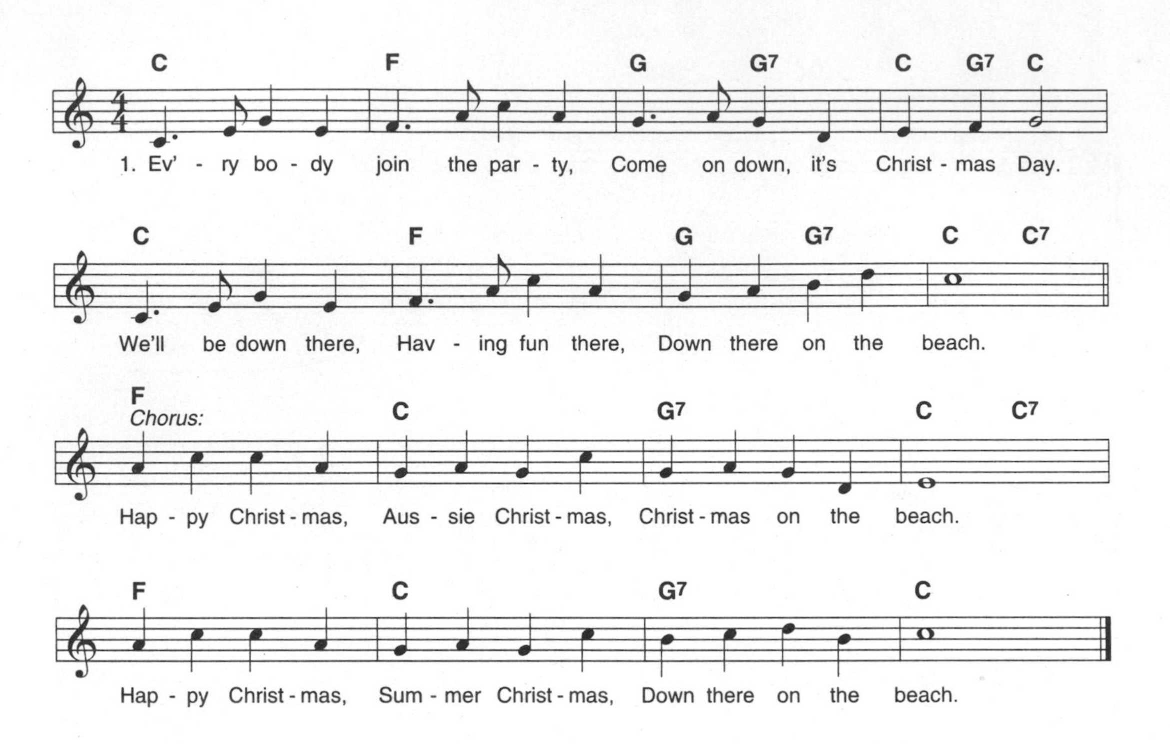

2.We've cold turkey,
Lots of salads
And a cool iced Christmas pud.
Lots to eat and
Cool canned drinks and
We'll have lots of fun.

Chorus

3.Gentle breezes
From the ocean
Take the heat out of the sun.
We'll go surfing,
Sailing, swimming,
Join us on the beach.

Chorus

4.As the sun sinks
In the ev'ning
We'll enjoy a bar-b-q:
Then sing carols
Christmas carols,
Join us on the beach.

Chorus

Merry Christmas

Music by William G. James and words by John Wheeler

2.Golden day,
When we say,
Merry, merry Christmas,
In the street,
Where we meet,
Merry, merry, merry Christmas.
And with pride
Far and wide
All our homes adorning;
Earth and sky
Sound the cry,
'Welcome Christmas morning.'

3.So with joy,
Man and boy,
Sing with us together;
On this morn,
Christ was born,
Merry, merry, merry Christmas,
Raise the song,
Loud and strong,
In the shining weather.
Joy bells ring,
Christ is King,
Merry, merry, merry Christmas.

Across the nations

Music by Douglas Coombes and words by Fiona Shore

2.Stamp your feet
With the beat,
Join our celebrations.
Hear the joyful sound we make
Ring out across the nations.

Chorus

3.Clap your hands
In all lands,
Join our celebrations.
Hear the rhythm that we make
Ring out across the nations.

Chorus

4.Here we stand
Hand in hand,
Join our celebrations.
Feel the friendships that we make
Flow out across the nations.

Chorus

If Jesus was born today

Carole Henderson Begg

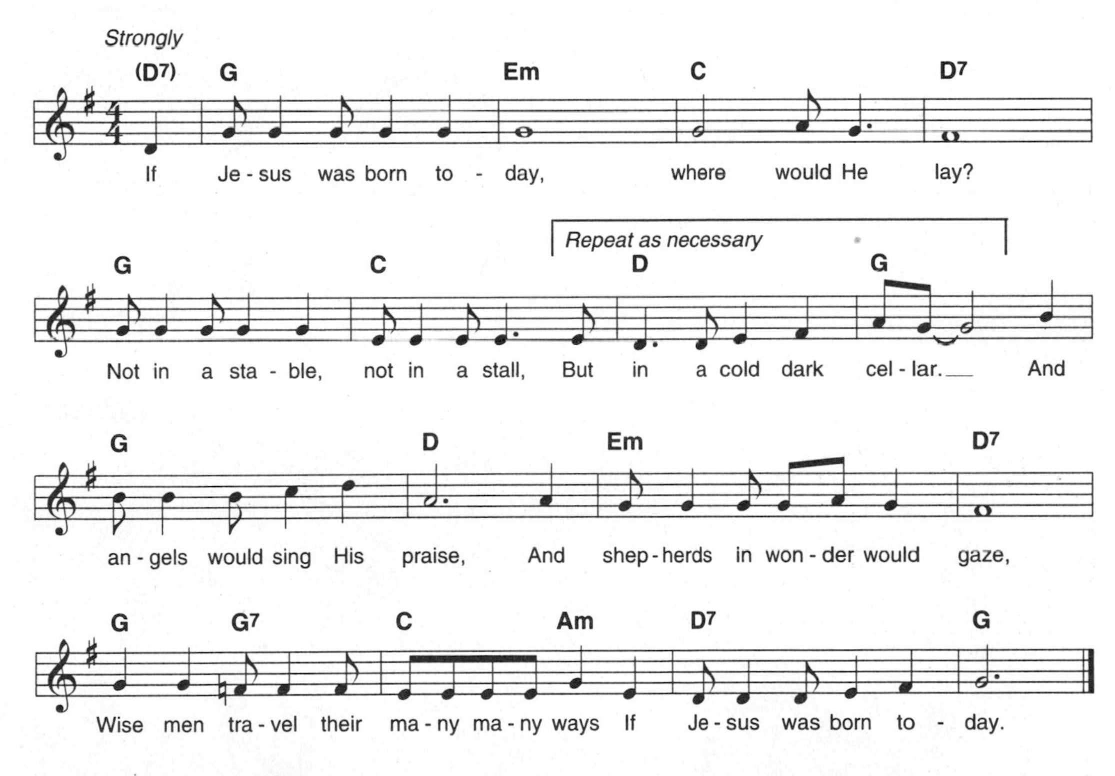

2.If Jesus was born to-day, where would he lay?
Not in a stable, not in a stall,
But in a poor mud shelter,
Or in a cold dark cellar;
And angels would sing in praise...

3.But in a down-town hovel,
Or in...

4.But in a pine log cabin,
Or in...

5.But in a tent of goats' skin,
Or in...

6.But in a Chinese sam pan,
Or in...

Comin' to dis world

Ian Henderson Begg

2.Shepherds witnessed,
Comin' to dis world:
Wise men worshipped,
Comin' to dis world:
Bands of angels,
Comin' to dis world:
Sang his glory,
Comin' to dis world.

Chorus

3.Whole world's singin',
Comin' to dis world:
'Bout de baby,
Comin' to dis world:
Come to save us,
Comin' to dis world:
Come to lead us,
Comin' to dis world.

Chorus

4.Mary's baby,
Comin' to dis world:
We'll wait for you,
Comin' to dis world:
Hear our singin',
Comin' to dis world:
Come embrace us,
Comin' to dis world.

Chorus

Issa alei salaam (a Hindi carol)

Nash Meghji

Translation:
Jesus, may peace be upon Him

1.In an ordinary house in Nazareth
Appeared the Angel Gabriel
And gave to a chaste, holy girl called Mary
The message of God.

2.You will be the mother
Of a heavenly child
Whose name will be Jesus
And He will be the redeemer of all beings.

The aid worker's Christmas

Gerald Haigh

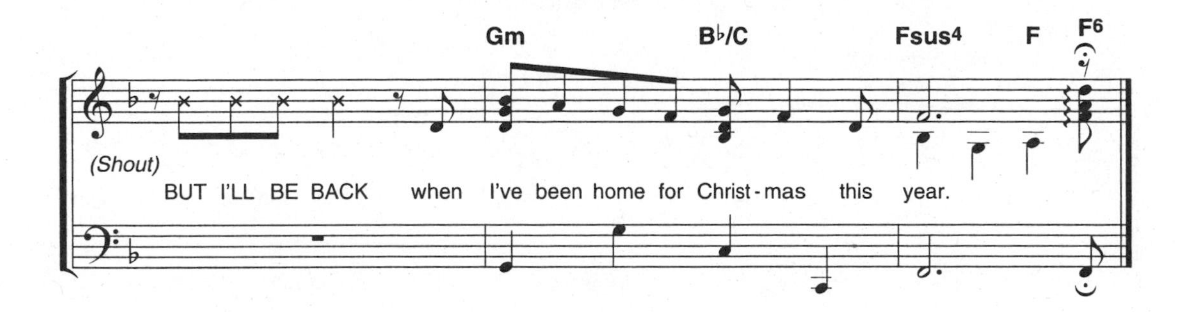

2.I first came out here feeling so strange
But you all made me welcome straight away.
Now my work's so rewarding that I never want to change
I look forward to the challenge each day.

3.It's three years now since I first left my home;
I was missing some good old homely talk.
I'll explore all the places where my friends and I would roam
And I'll smell the English fields as we walk.

4.The choir will sing in the church that I knew
And we'll walk arm in arm down country lanes,
There'll be Christmas dinner and perhaps some presents too
And I will not even mind if it rains.

5.But don't you fret now, I'm coming right back
When the New Year party's over, just you see.
I'll be feeling bored – I'll be going up to pack
For I'll hear this country calling to me.

6.My plane is waiting, goodbye now, old friend.
It's my flight that they're calling, can't you hear?
Mum and dad will be waiting when I reach my journey's end
For I'm going home for Christmas *(clap)*
I'll have a lovely Christmas *(clap)*
A good old family Christmas *(clap)*
I'm going home for Christmas this year.
(shout back) But I'll be back –
When I've been home for Christmas this year.

Chris has been in Africa for three years, working on an agricultural project, helping people to develop ways of improving their crops. He loves his work, and his last two Christmases in Africa were memorable. This year, though, he realises that his parents miss him, and some of his childhood memories come back. He decides to go home for a couple of weeks. Simeon, his driver and general assistant, drives him to the airport in the Land Rover.

Father Christmas rock around Europe

Ann Bryant

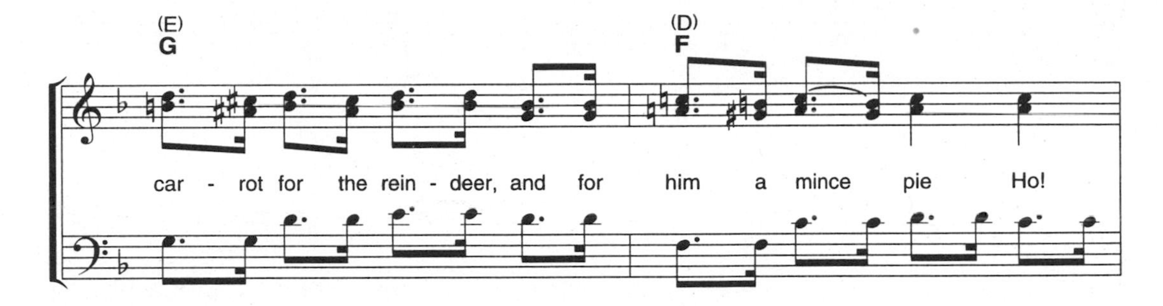

3.No, he doesn't come by bus and he doesn't come by train.
In Holland he comes sailing in a steamboat up from Spain.
And his name is Sinter Klaus and he rides a white horse.
Giddy up! Got the presents? Yes, of course!

4.In Germany outside your bedroom door you leave a shoe,
And Weihnachtsmann, he knows all about you.
If you're bad he leaves a stick and if you're good he leaves a sweet.
Hey hey! What a day! What a treat!

5.Here he comes from the sky and they call him Père Noël
He is flying with the reindeers, you can hear the sleigh bell.
Yes, France is where you leave a cake and hope that Père Noël will take it.
If he does he'll leave a tale to tell.

6.In Denmark children are dancing round the tree,
Saying here's a heart for you and here's a drum for me.
Then they hear the sound of Nissen, his footsteps coming near,
Quick! Fetch the rice pudding and beer!

Repeat verse 1

Alle Jahre Wieder (Every year He comes again)

Traditional German carol, translated by Ann Bryant

2.When he comes to see me
He will hold my hand.
Jesus is the Christ child,
King of every land.

3.When His birthday's over
For another year
Still He stays beside me
And still I feel Him near.

This is the first carol young children in Germany are taught.

Juletraeet med sin pynt (The Christmas tree and its decorations)

Traditional Danish carol, translated by Ann Bryant

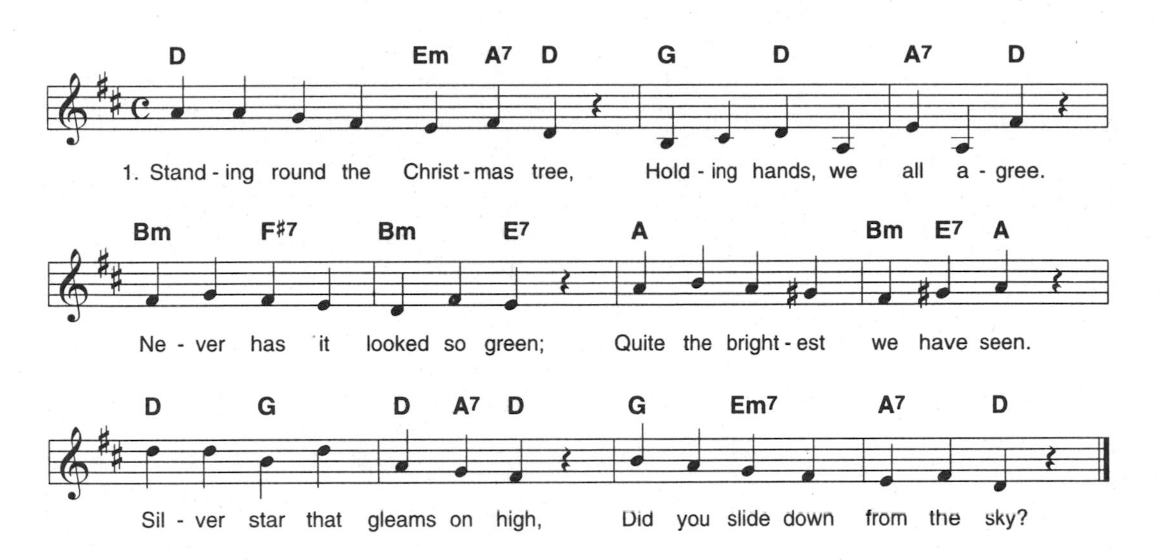

2.Fragile cones and paper curls,
Gently fashioned wispy whirls;
There up high a tiny bird
Softly spreads the Christmas word.
'Who has made these perfect things
For our Christmas tree?' he sings.

3.Now we touch our tree with light,
All the candles burning bright.
Smell the pinewood smoky brown,
Hear the needles flutter down.
In our winter world today
Can you smell a summer's day?

4.If you're quiet you'll hear with me
The message from our Christmas tree.
'Though the darker days are here
Lighter days are drawing near
From his hiding place, the sun
Sends his love to everyone.'

Christmas tree

David Moses

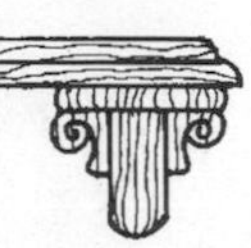

2.His sleigh bells ring with a merry ching ching
As up and away his reindeer spring.
Gee-hup, gee-ho, how swift they go
Over the ice and drifts of snow.
For he must call on one and all
With presents for you and me
For he is Santa Claus's man
Kris Kringle with his Christmas tree.

3.With cakes and plums, trumpets and drums
And lots of lovely things he comes.
There's rhymes to say and games to play,
We'll have a good time on Christmas day.
I think he's near, he'll soon appear
And soon his jolly face we'll see.
So welcome Santa Claus's man
Kris Kringle with his Christmas tree.

Kris Kringle is Santa Claus's trusted helper and is usually associated with North America or Scandinavia. This, however, is a traditional English song. It comes from North Yorkshire where it accompanies a Morris dance.

Il est né le divin enfant
(He was born the child divine)

Traditional French carol, translated by Ann Bryant

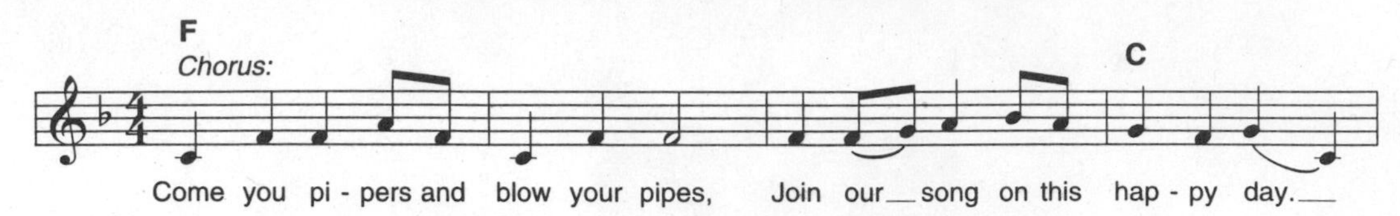

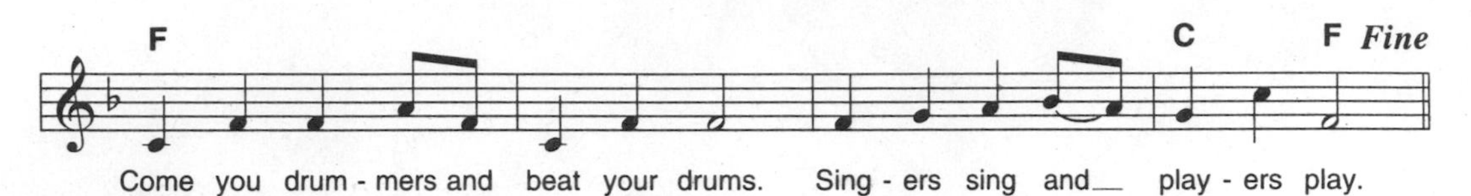

2.In a stable he was born
In a manger filled with straw.
In a stable he was born,
Born to reign but born so poor.

Chorus

3.From the East came the three wise men.
Bearing gifts they journeyed far.
From the East came the three wise men
Guided by the silver star.

Chorus

4.God of Gods and King of Kings
Reigning over everyone.
Just a tiny little child
Reigning over everyone.

Chorus

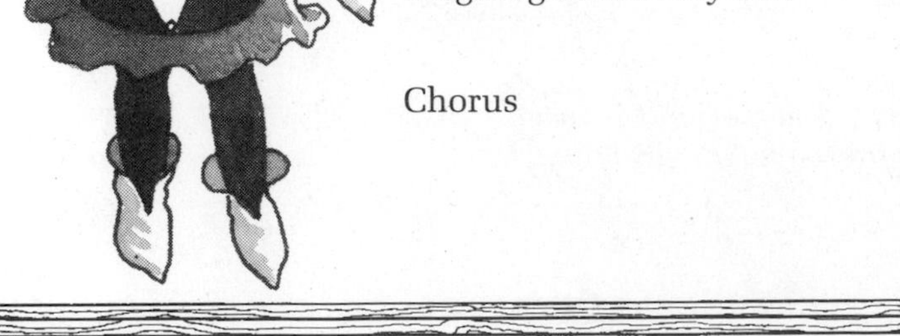

Hoe leit dit kindeken
(How this little child lays)

Traditional Dutch carol, translated by Ann Bryant

2.Shepherds keep watch by the light of the moon.
Come, little shepherd boy, come play your tune to Him.
Hush, baby Jesus, you'll be asleep soon.

Chorus

3.Angels from heaven, your sweet voices bring.
Join in the song that the children all sing to Him.
This is a lullaby, just for our King.

Chorus

Jeg er saa glad hver jukelveld (I'm so happy every Christmas Eve)

Traditional Norwegian carol, translated by Ann Bryant

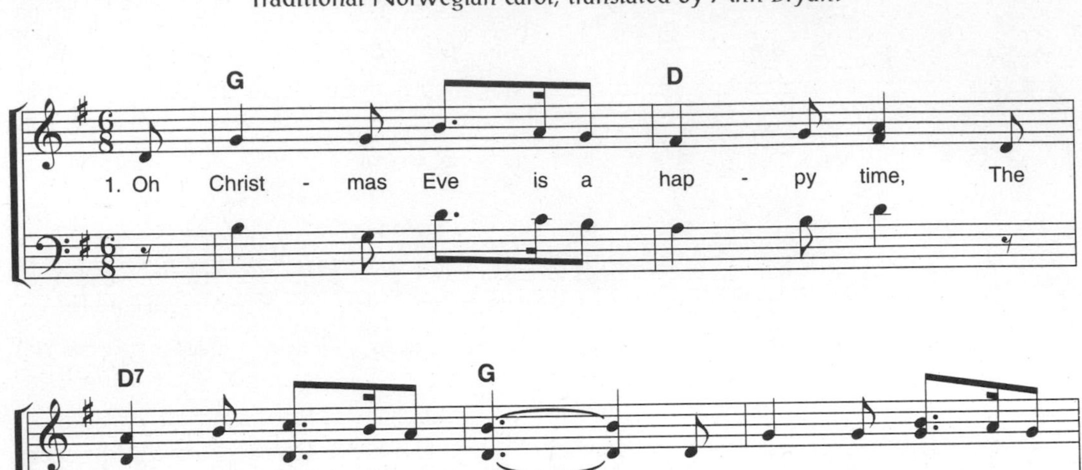

2.The mightiest castle in all the sky
Sent down for us on the earth
A baby child to be King of Kings.
How great the Bethlehem birth.

3.And still he hears all the prayers we pray
And still He sees us below.
There's not a child that He does not see,
And none that he does not know.

4.Oh Christmas Eve is a happy time
We think of God's own son.
His hands spread open, and from them falls
His love for everyone.

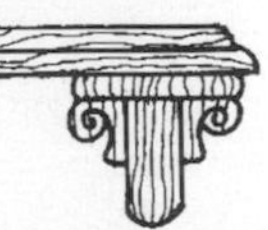

The stranger in the blizzard

Ian Henderson Begg

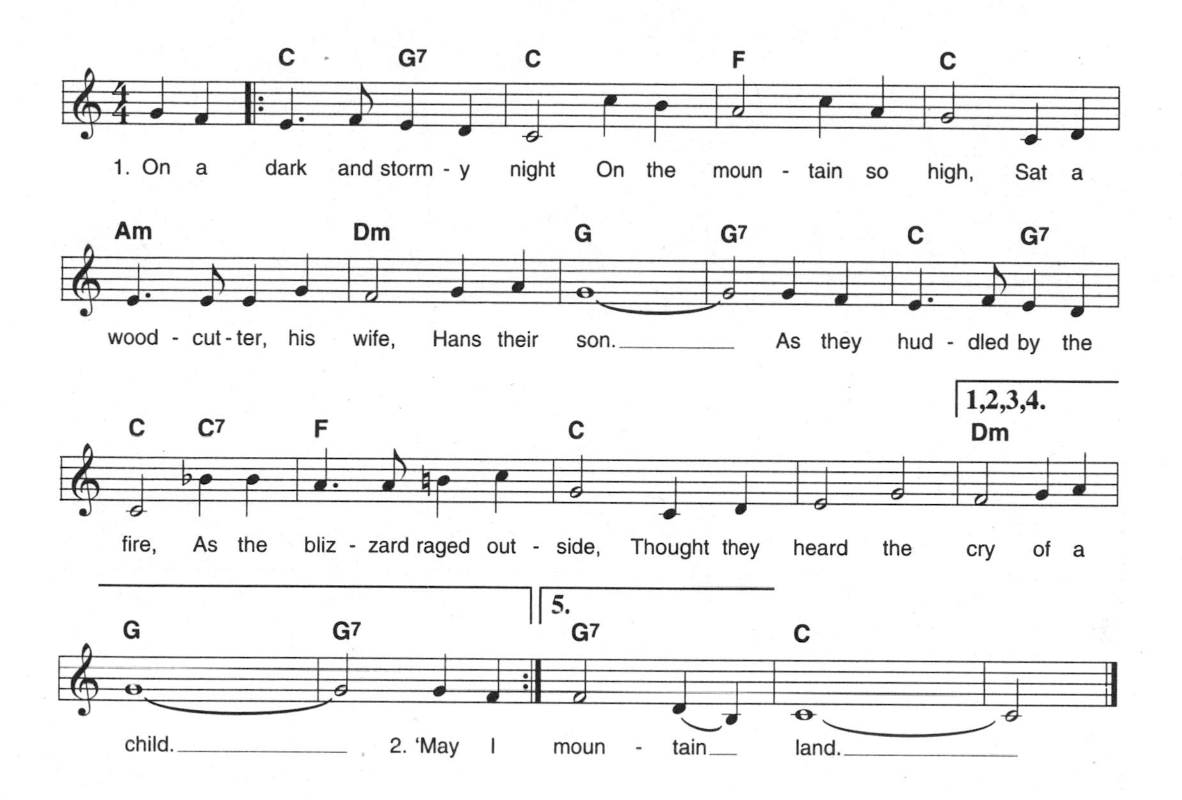

2.'May I come in from the cold,
On this dark, stormy night,
Will you shelter me and let
Me get warm?'
'Come inside,' the poor man said,
'Come and share our humble meal,
You can sleep with Hans by the fire.'

3.In the morning when they woke
He had gone, like the storm.
Though they searched for him he'd
Vanished away.
Then outside to Hans' surprise
Was the boy, who came to him
With a branch of fir from a tree.

4.'Take this branch,' the stranger said,
'Laden with apples red.
It will always carry gifts
For you all,
For last night you took me in
And you gave me food and warmth,
When you could have turned me away.'

5.Then the stranger turned and left,
And it seemed to Hans
That the sun shone like a halo
Round his head.
But the wise ones knew his name,
Knew the saviour had come,
And he'd blessed their mountain land.

This carol tells a traditional Austrian folk tale about the visit of the Christ Child to a lonely woodcutter's house. Austrians decorate a fir tree with apples ready for the Christ Child should he knock on their door.

Worlds apart

Catherine Morrell

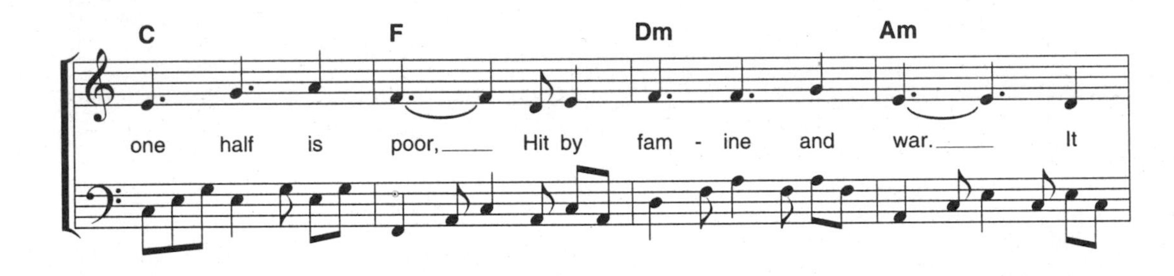

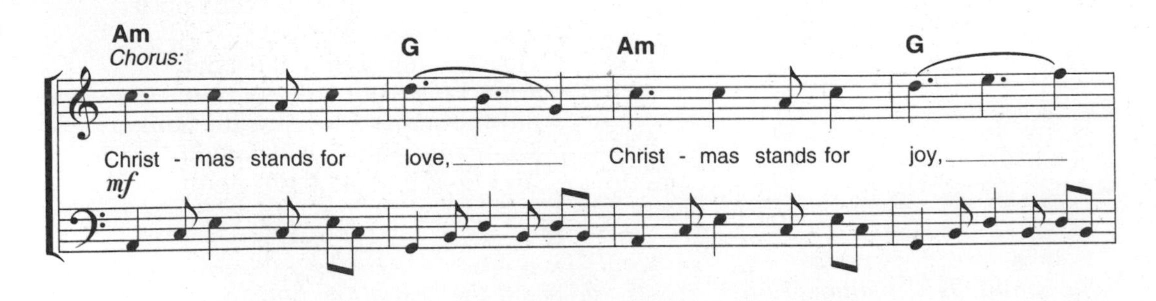

2.Ring Christmas bells
And sing joyous Noels
And let's all celebrate near and far.
Just pause for a thought
At the presents you've bought
And think of those brave people
Worlds apart.

Chorus

Join hands

Lonee Hewitt

2.
F
F7
B♭
lives.
God gave us all these
C
F
B♭
things that we need to make us hap - py, All these things are
1.
2.
C
F
F
C7
free to us all.
God gave us all.
F
D.𝄋 to 𝄌 then Coda
If
Coda
F
C
F
har - mo - ny.

Merry Christmas

German folk song, arranged by Margaret I. Fletcher and Margaret Conboy Denison

CHRISTMAS AT HOME AND SCHOOL
Christmas bells
Lisa Mackenzie
C Em F C
Group 1
Ring the Christ - mas bells to - day, Ring the Christ - mas bells,
Group 2
Ding, Dong, Ding, Dong,
Group 3
Christ - mas bells are gai - ly ring - ing,
Group 4
La la la la, la la la la, la la la la, la la la la,
G7 C G7 C
Christ - mas time is here a - gain, Ring the Christ - mas bells.
Ding, Dong, Ding, Dong.
Hear the child - ren bright - ly sing - ing.
la la la la, la la la la, la la la la, la la la.

The Christmas alphabet

Paul Sudlow

A7 D D7 G D B
leaves ne - ver fall. S is for Shep - herds who care for their sheep, The
G A7 G D7 G F C
first to see Je - sus as He lay a - sleep. T is for Tin - sel all
D.C. to ⊕ then Coda
Gsus4 G7 C Dm7 G7 Am C D7 Gsus4 G7
round the tree, With pre - sents put round it for you and me.
Coda (optional)
C Am C F C Am
Group 1:
Christ - mas comes but once a year: We wish you all the
Group 2: Christ - mas comes but once a year: We

2.'M' is for Mary the Mother so mild,
In the stable holding her child.
'A' is for Angel with tidings of joy,
Bringing news of the baby boy.
'S' is for Star whose silv'ry light
Guided wise men through the dark that night.

Christmas thoughts

Ian Henderson Begg

2. Yet it wasn't long ago
In this land they say
Christmas wasn't as we know it now,
It was a normal day.
Those who cared might meet and sing
Hymns of praise and love
To the babe of Bethlehem,
Son of God.

3. As the day comes nearer now,
As excitement lives,
May we share with those we love
The love that Jesus gives.
And through all the revelry
May we know and share
That true spirit of Christmas time,
Love and care.

Christmas card

Gillian Parker

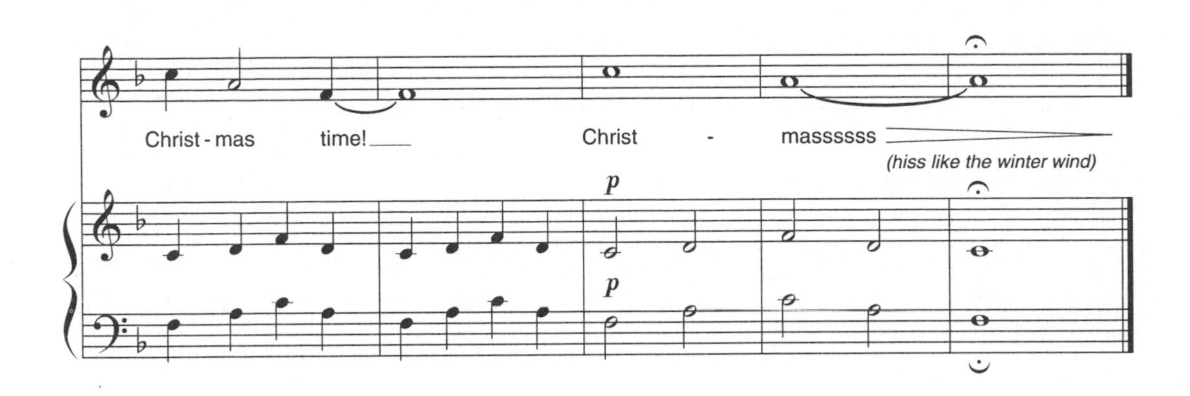

Percussion accompaniment:

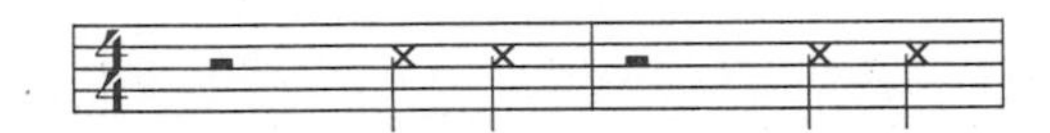

Indian Bells for ostinato figure throughout

Chime bars, glocks, xylophones playing the following: (Piano optional)

Aren't you glad they've cancelled Christmas?

David Moses

2. Aren't you glad, aren't you glad that Santa Claus is locked in jail?
Aren't you glad, aren't you glad they've tied up all his reindeer's tails?
They've opened up your presents, and thrown them all away.
Ain't that queer, dear oh dear, we will have a lovely time this year.

3. Aren't you glad, aren't you glad there's no more fun and no more treats?
Aren't you glad, aren't you glad there's only dry, brown bread to eat?
There's no more Christmas crackers, and nothing on T.V.
Oh, how drear, dear oh dear, we will have a lovely time this year.

4. Aren't you glad, aren't you glad it's not the truth I'm singing?
Aren't you glad, aren't you glad outside church bells are ringing?
There's mince pies in the oven, and presents on the tree,
So let's hear a nice big cheer (HURRAY). We're going to have a lovely time this year.

The Nth day of Christmas

Chris Williams

2.When did you first hear the singing of a Christmas song?
In September, October or was it in June?
When did you last hear the silence of the falling snow?
In November, December or at the last blue moon?
Many may try....

The robin

Ann Bryant

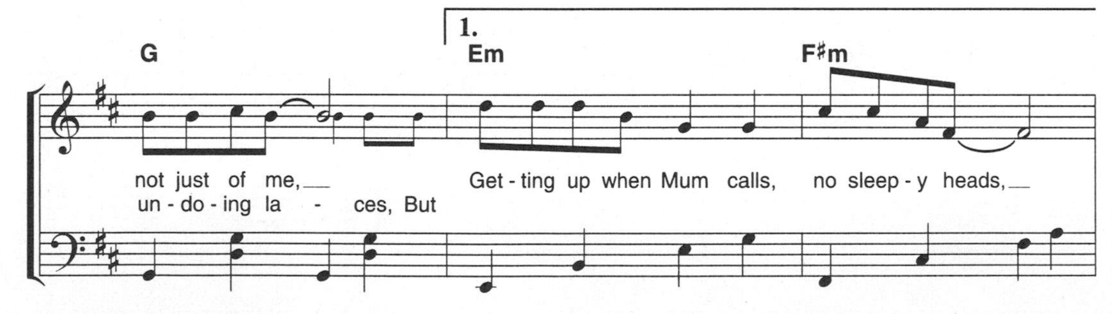

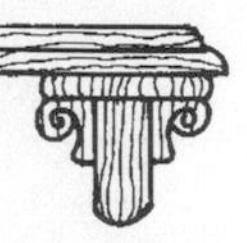

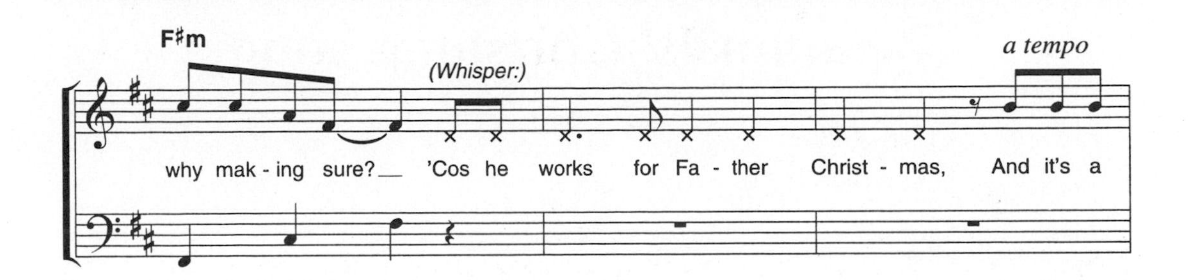

2. There's a robin looking at me. Where?
Through the window, can't you see. Yeah!
He's making sure that we care
About brushing our teeth and washing our faces,
Taking our shoes off, undoing laces,
But why is he watching, why making sure?

Whisper: 'Cos he works for Father Christmas
And it's a Father Christmas special Children's Law!

A Christmas round

Traditional

The animals' Christmas song

Jean Gilbert

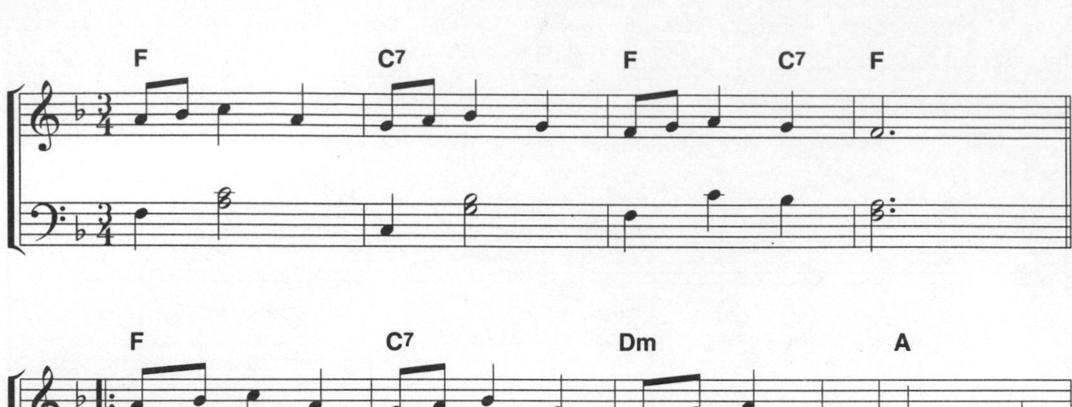

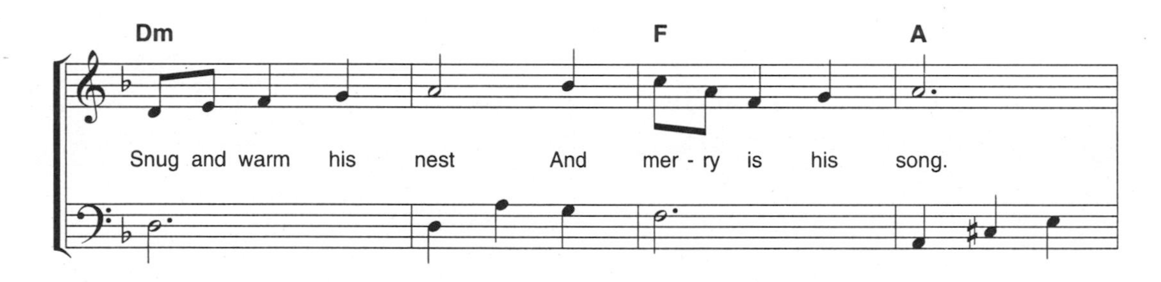

Coda

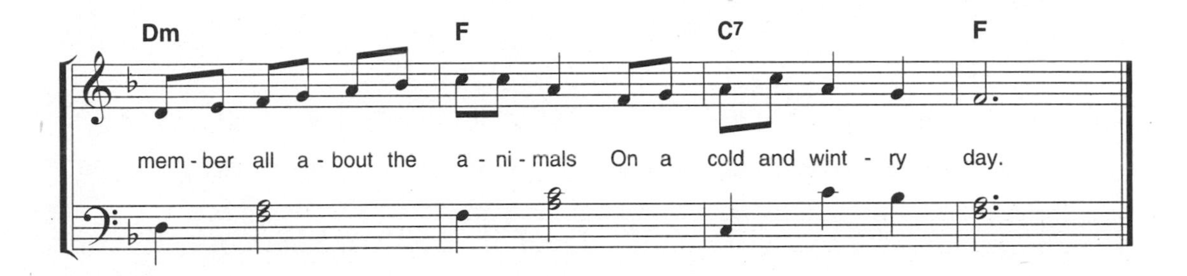

2.Christmas time is here again
And children sing and play,
But what about the mountain reindeer
On a cold and wintry day?

Thick and warm his coat,
His legs are straight and strong.
See him run and leap,
See him galloping along.

Chorus

3.Christmas time is here again
And children sing and play,
But what about the lovely grey geese
On a cold and wintry day?

Feathers soft and warm
And wings to fly up high.
Time to seek the sun
Away into the sky.

Chorus

4.Christmas time is here again
And children sing and play,
But what about the farmer's woolly sheep
On a cold and wintry day?

Though the winds may blow
Their fleece will keep them warm.
Farmers bring them in
To shelter from the storm.

Chorus

5.Christmas time is here again
And children sing and play,
Remember all about the animals
On a cold and wintry day.

Many other animals could be included in this song. Use the framework of the chorus to introduce the ones that your children would like to sing about. Let them help you make up the verses.

What is all the noise about?

David Moses

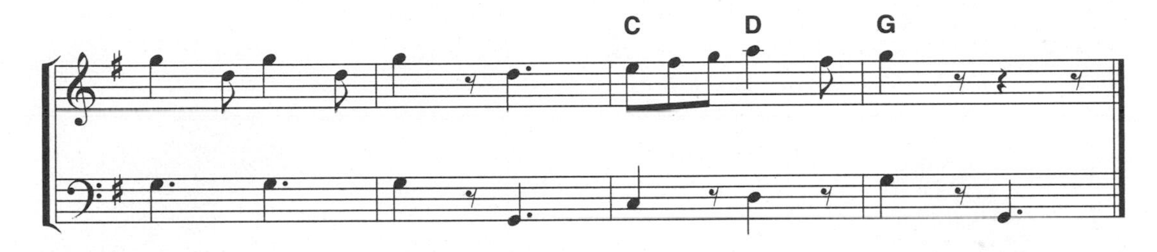

2.On the tree there will be
Coloured lights all glittery,
Paper chains, party games, lovely things to eat,
And you get so excited you
Feel all jittery
Under the tree there may be
A special Christmas treat.

Chorus

3.They remind us a baby was
Born in Bethlehem
Many many years ago, so the story tells,
And the angels appeared in the
Sky round Bethlehem
Singing on high. That is why
We ring the Christmas bells.

Chorus

4.As they ring, people sing
Of the kings and shepherds who
Saw a child, meek and mild in a manger lie.
Let the bells ring around you,
And if you happen to
Hear them chime at Christmas time,
You'll know the reason why.

The Christmas train

Ann Bryant

2. Come and ride on the Christmas train,
We're going to see the angels,
We're going to see the angels.
Come and ride on the Christmas train,
We're going to see the angels in the sky.

3. We're going to see the shepherds on the hill.

4. We're going to see the wise men with their gifts.

5. We're going to see the stable under the star.

6. *Repeat verse one.*

Christmas time

Alan Simmons

The carol singers

Gillian Parker

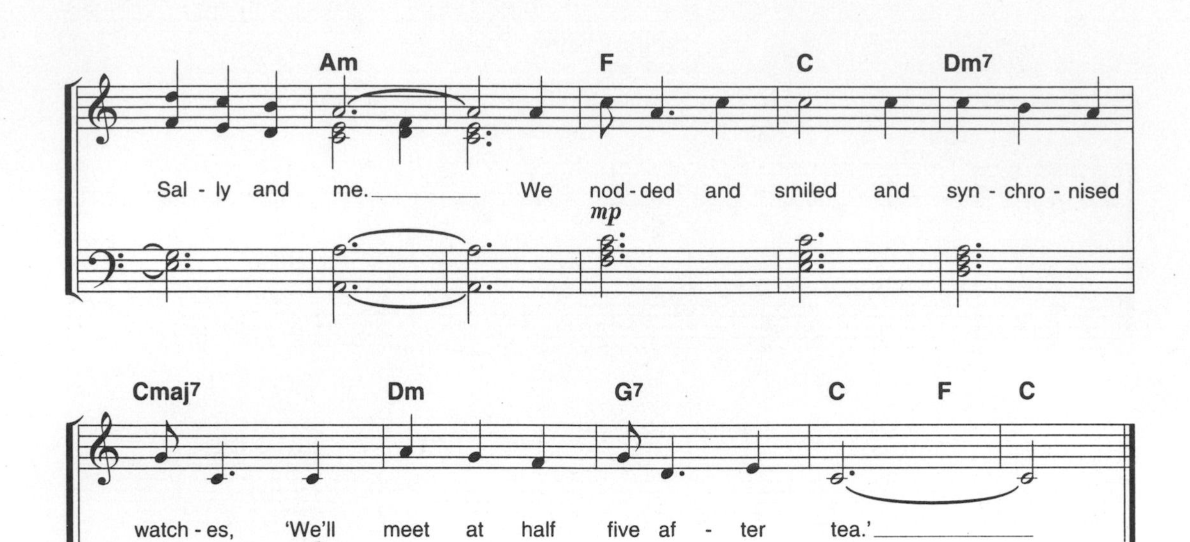

2.It started to rain, then it started to snow,
I rang up Sue, Sally and Fi.
'We can't go tonight, it's too cold and too wet,'
Said Sally to Fi, Sue and me.
'My Mum says it's not safe to go after dark,'
Said Sue to Fi, Sally and me.
We nodded and smiled and hung up our 'phones
Then sat down and finished our tea.

3.We met in the playground at school the next day,
Sue, Sally, Fiona and me.
'I did want to go and sing carols last night,'
Said Sally to Fi, Sue and me.
'Let's go to the hospital, sing to the patients,'
Said Sue to Fi, Sally and me.
We nodded and smiled and said we would meet there
This Sunday at quarter past three.

The addresses on lines 3 and 4 in verse one may be changed to any local names as desired, as can the names of the four children (providing the number of syllables is the same).

Christmas squiggles

Ann Bryant

Brightly

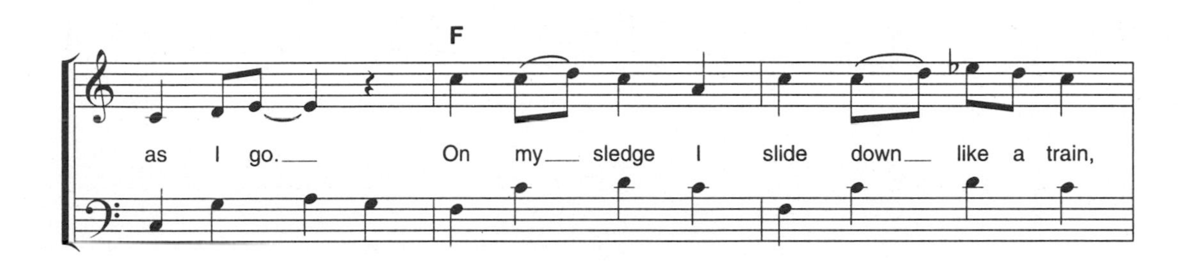

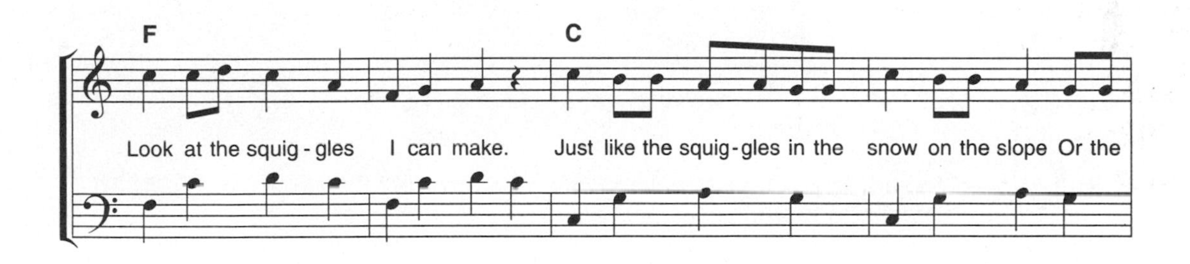

This round can be sung in eight parts, starting at intervals of one bar. To finish, hold the first note of any bar.

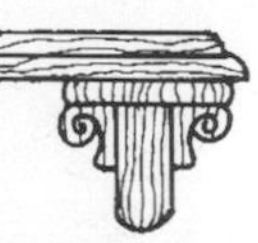

Frosty

Clive Barnwell

2. With his woolly scarf to keep him warm,
His hat to shield him from the storm,
And his umbrella by his side,
Frosty will be safe tonight.

When the sun comes out his eyes of coals
Send snow tears down his carrot nose,
And the garden shows where snow has cleared
That's when Frosty disappears.

Chorus

Christmas daydreams

Ann Bryant

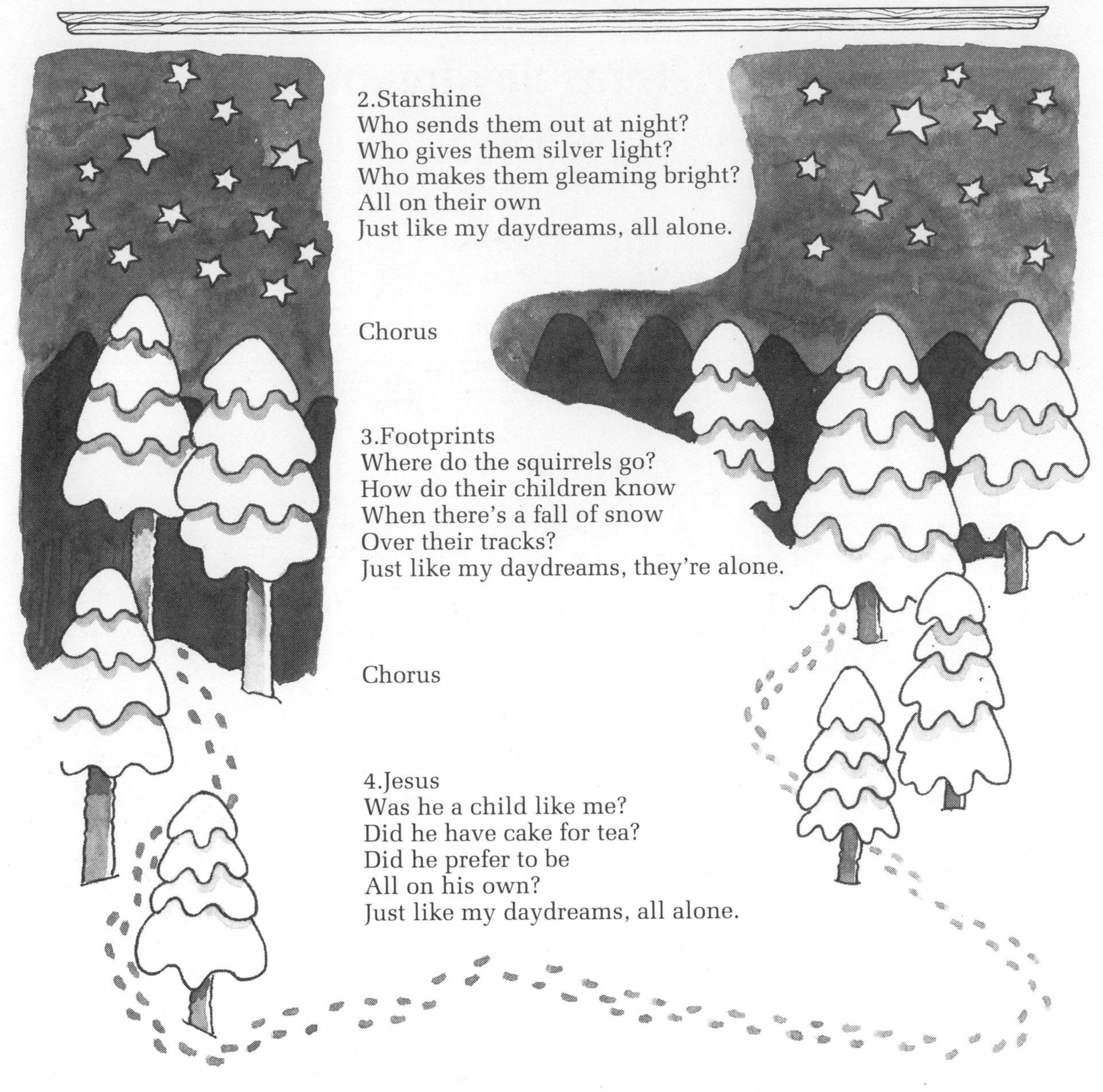

2.Starshine
Who sends them out at night?
Who gives them silver light?
Who makes them gleaming bright?
All on their own
Just like my daydreams, all alone.

Chorus

3.Footprints
Where do the squirrels go?
How do their children know
When there's a fall of snow
Over their tracks?
Just like my daydreams, they're alone.

Chorus

4.Jesus
Was he a child like me?
Did he have cake for tea?
Did he prefer to be
All on his own?
Just like my daydreams, all alone.

Round the Christmas tree

Alan Simmons

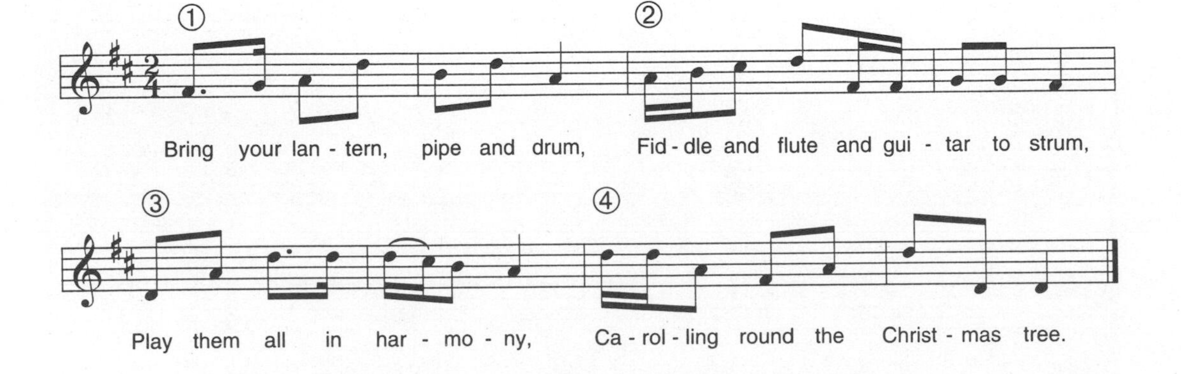

Christmas tree

Peter Morrell

2.Now Martin Luther walking out upon one Christmas Eve,
Looked up to heav'n and saw the stars in total disbelief.
The sight of all those stars on high
Reminded him of Jesus Christ,
And so with candles all alight
A fir tree shone like stars that night.

Chorus

3.In England Christmas trees arrived in Queen Victoria's time,
Prince Albert introduced them and the Queen said, 'They look fine.'
At Windsor Castle one was seen
The very first fit for a Queen,
And so in eighteen forty one
This old tradition was begun.

Chorus (*without spoken lines*)

Decorate the tree

Ian Henderson Begg

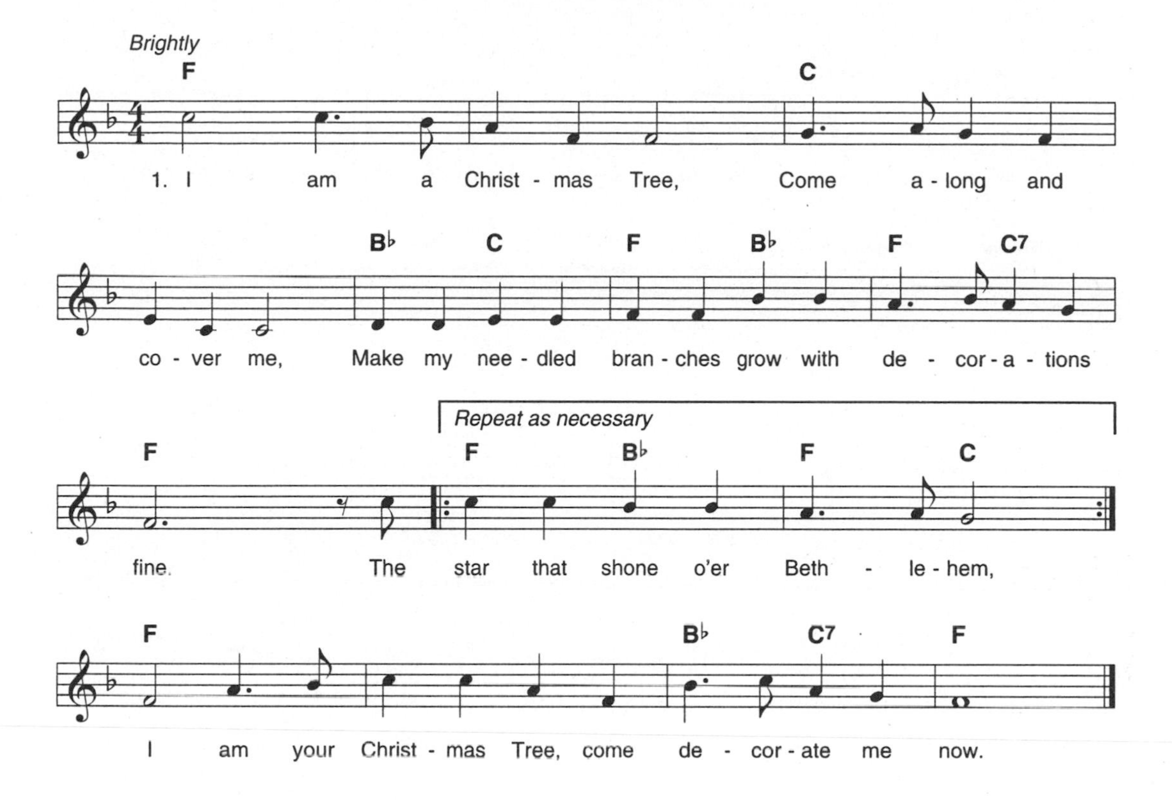

2.I am a Christmas tree, come along and cover me.
Make my needled branches grow with decorations fine.
Tinsel frost, it's cold again;
The star that shone o'er Bethlehem;
I am your Christmas tree, come decorate me now.

3.*add* 'Twinkling lights to show the way'

4.*add* 'Baby Jesus born that day'

5.*add* 'Choc'late makes a tasty treat'

6.I am a Christmas Tree, come along and cover me.
Make my needled branches grow with decorations fine.
Baubles for the world complete;
Choc'late makes a tasty treat;
Baby Jesus born that day;
Twinkling lights to show the way;
Tinsel frost, it's cold again;
Star that shone o'er Bethlehem;
I am your Christmas tree, come decorate me now.

Buying presents

Lisa Mackenzie

2. What can I buy for Grandma, and little brother Pete?
Now I know why Mummy says, 'It's hard to make ends meet!'
I must remember Auntie and Uncle Jim as well
I'll even buy my pussy cat a collar with a bell. Chorus

Christmas market

Gillian Parker

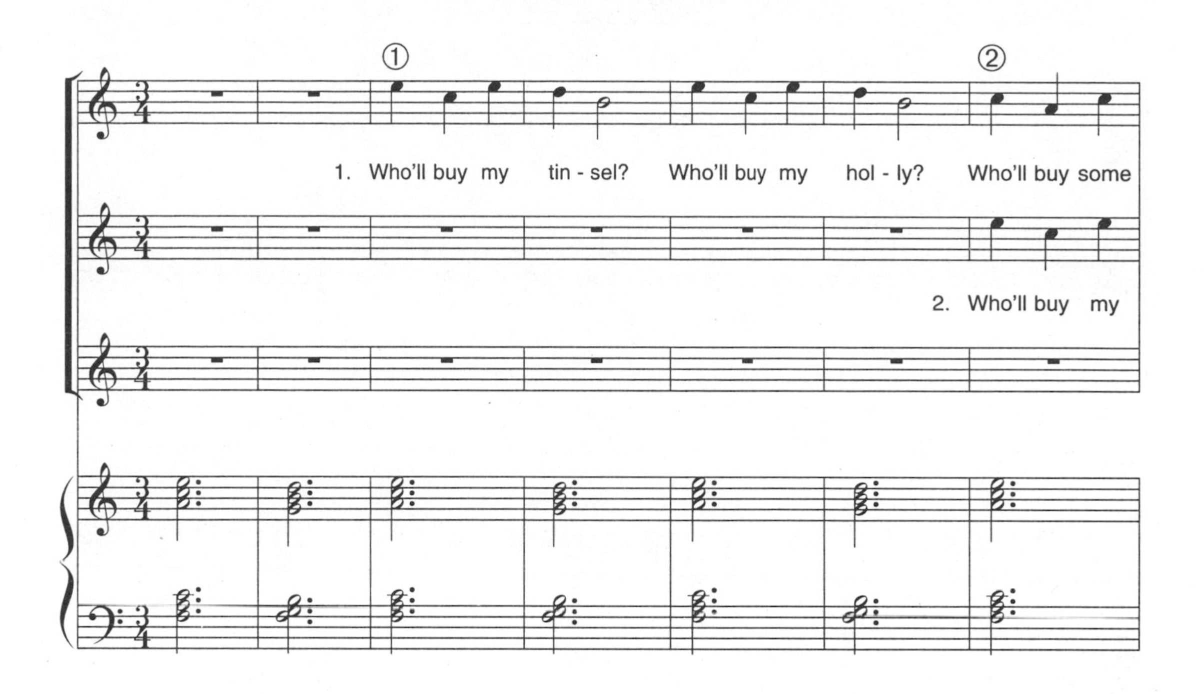

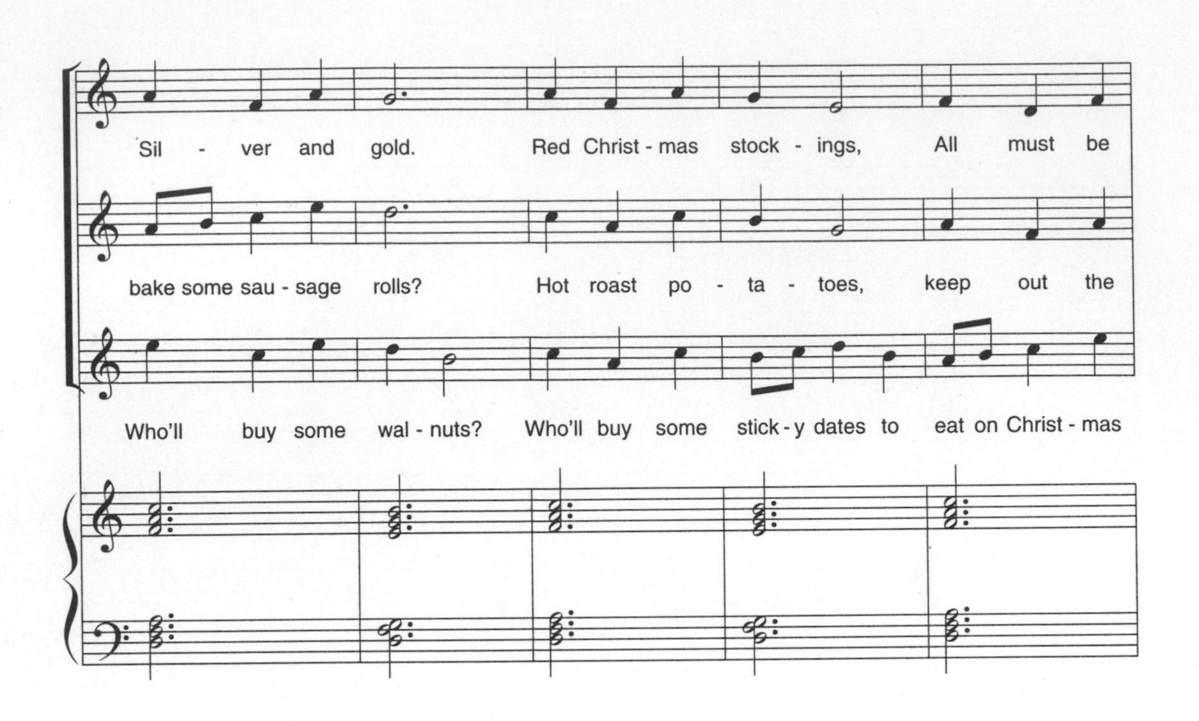
Sil - ver and gold. Red Christ - mas stock - ings, All must be
bake some sau - sage rolls? Hot roast po - ta - toes, keep out the
Who'll buy some wal - nuts? Who'll buy some stick - y dates to eat on Christ - mas

sold to - day, Christ - mas gifts for you.
cold, Chick - ens and tur - keys, All must be sold to - day, Christ - mas
Eve? Fresh - ly baked chest - nuts, Too hot to hold, Last box of crack - ers,

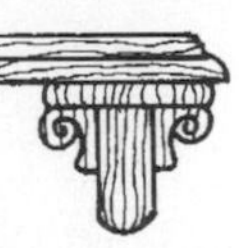

lunch for you.
All must be sold to-day, Christ - mas cheer to you!
JUICY MARROW
PUMP-KINS
FRESH MANGOES
KIWI FRUIT FRESH
PAPAYAS
HOLLY WREATHS
Plum Pud

Santa's supermarket

Anonymous

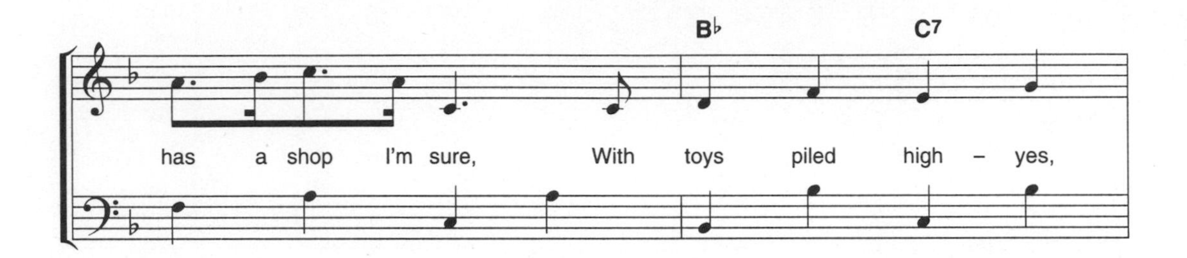

2.Now I'm six and I can write,
I think, I think, I think I might
Make a list this very night,
For Santa's supermarket.

3.On this list I think there'll be
Toys for Timothy, Jane and Lee.
With something special just for me,
From Santa's supermarket.

4.I wish, how I wish that I
Could fly to Santa-land on high,
And fill my trolley to the sky
In Santa's supermarket.

My gran wants an Action Man

Debbie Campbell

2.My brother Victor wants a boa constrictor
But a snake would be a mistake.
For wouldn't it be shocking
If it wriggled out his stocking
And hid inside the Christmas cake?
My Uncle Ray wants a new toupée
'Cos he hasn't any hair.
Mum says buy her something to wear.
Dad says he doesn't care. We don't believe him.
Dad says he doesn't care. He's only kidding.
Dad says he doesn't care. So there.

This song can be divided up to enable individual children to make each request. Alternative words can be made up about friends or family.

Christmas shopping

David Moses

C
toy shop,
Me oh my.
Stop-ping at the toy shop,
F
There are dolls,
aaaah...
Me oh my.
There are dolls,
C
There are trains [toot toot]
There are
aaaah...
There are trains [toot toot]
Dm7
C
whis-tles [whistle]
There are planes
There are whist-les [whistle]
G7
D.C.
[neaow]
(spoken:) but I don't think dad will want any of those for a present
so
There are planes [neaow]

Chorus

2.Walking down the high street
What's there to buy?
Stopping at the pet shop
Me oh my.
There are dogs...WROW WROW
There are cats... MIAOW
There are snakes... *(hiss)*
There are rats... *(squeak)*

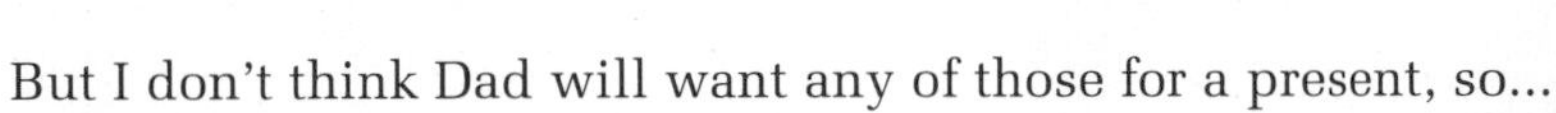

But I don't think Dad will want any of those for a present, so...

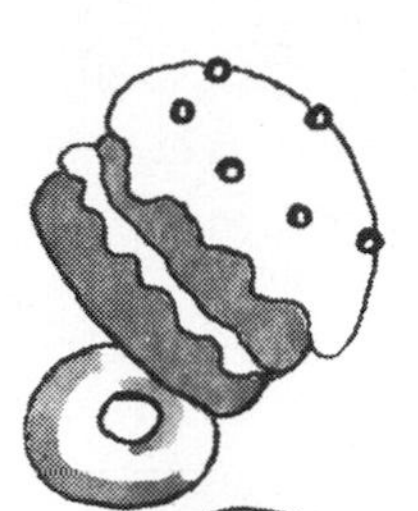

Chorus

3.Walking down the high street
What's there to buy?
Stopping at the cake shop
Me oh my.
There are cream cakes... mmmmm
Apple flan
There are doughnuts
Filled with jam

But I don't think Dad should have any of those for a present, so...

Chorus

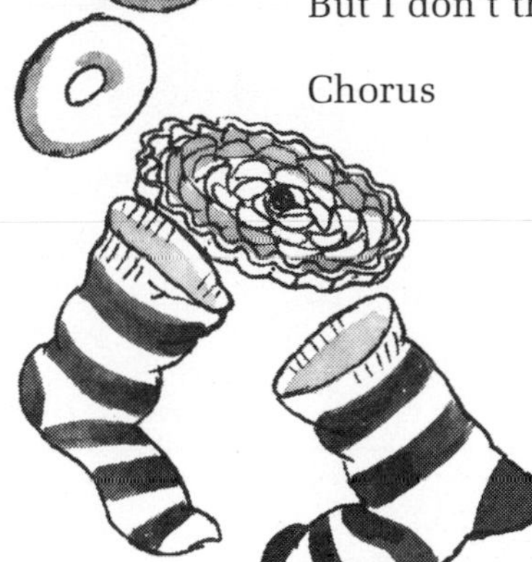

4.Walking down the high street
What's there to buy?
Stopping at the clothes shop
Me oh my.
There are socks... yeah, that's what I got him last year,
And he said it was the best present he'd ever had, so...

Wrap them up in paper, I hope they will be
The nicest Christmas present Dad has ever had.

An old man lives in Lollipop Land

David Moses

2.Now this old man has a coat of red *(repeat)*
Sing high *(repeat)* sing low *(repeat)*
Sing high *(repeat)* sing low *(repeat)*
This coat of red *(repeat)*
Stops the old man from catching cold. *(repeat)*

3.Now this old man has a bell to ring *(repeat)*
Sing high *(repeat)* sing low *(repeat)*
Sing high *(repeat)* sing low *(repeat)*
This funny old man *(repeat)*
Rings his bell wherever he goes. *(repeat)*

4.Now this old man has a reindeer sleigh *(repeat)*
Sing high *(repeat)* sing low *(repeat)*
Sing high *(repeat)* sing low *(repeat)*
This reindeer sleigh *(repeat)*
Glides across the ice and snow. *(repeat)*

5.This reindeer sleigh has presents on the back *(repeat)*
Sing high *(repeat)* sing low *(repeat)*
Sing high *(repeat)* sing low *(repeat)*
There's presents on the back *(repeat)*
Who they're for, I just don't know. *(repeat)*

6.Now this old man has a very jolly laugh *(repeat)*
Sing high *(repeat)* sing low *(repeat)*
Sing high *(repeat)* sing low *(repeat)*
And when he laughs *(repeat)*
He goes 'Oh ho ho ho ho'. *(repeat)*

As a means of getting an audience instantly involved, the echo song is an excellent vehicle. It is also an entertaining way of developing children's aural perception, since they have to listen to the 'caller' and copy them exactly. The 'caller' could be an adult, a solo child or the performing group could be split into two smaller groups of equal size, each of which could take it in turns to be 'caller' for alternate verses. If an echo song is being performed as part of a public presentation, one class could be the caller and encourage the audience to sing the responses.

O Mister Builder (Santa's Song)

Ian Henderson Begg

2.Way back in the old days flues were built so wide
I could get in easily, I'd hardly touch the side.
They even built me footholds, a nice big hearth to boot.
Now when I can squeeze inside
I cover myself with soot. Chorus

3.Burglars and policemen, they must share the blame,
Making all the parents secure their window frames.
How can I fill the stockings if I can't get inside?
So hear me Mister Builder
Build your chimneys wide. Chorus

4.Modern central heating may be fine for you,
Vast estates of houses without a proper flue.
To vist all the children my chances must be small
When the only way in's the letter-box,
So hear me when I call... Chorus

Dear Santa Claus

Lisa Mackenzie

2.Mummy says to ask you for a present I would like,
I'd really like a skateboard or perhaps a mountain bike,
My brother wants a rocking horse and Daddy needs a drill,
And my mummy says she'll leave you a Christmas pie on the window sill.

Chorus

My name is Father Christmas

David Moses

2. There's a thing I see in gardens
When it's wintry and cold,
It sometimes wears a hat and scarf,
I think it's made of snow.

Chorus

3. On Christmas Day, at lunch time,
When you've finished your first course,
You might have this for afters
With custard or white sauce.

Chorus

4. There's things wrapped up in red and green,
In gold and pink and blue.
It's always nice to get them,
But it's nice to give them too.

Chorus

5. My name is Father Christmas,
And because you've been so bright,
I'll bring you all a present when I
Come on Christmas night.

I hope Santa Claus will come tonight

Clive Barnwell

1.
Dm G C Am F G
Claus will come to - night.___ (Ding - a - ding - a - ding - a - ding - dong - ding.)
Claus will come to - night.
2.
C F C F6 Fm6
___ Through the year I've tried to be___ As
Now that Christ - mas night is here___ You'll
C Em 1. Dm Ddim
good as I can pos - si - bly___ And I can on - ly hope That you have
fly the Christ - mas skies so clear___ And
C Cmaj7 2. D
seen me try - ing. in your sack of toys I hope there's
Dm G C Am Dm G
one just for me. San - ta, if you're a - bout___

2.Santa Claus, boots of black,
Will you bring your magic sack?
I hope Santa Claus will come tonight.
Ding-a-ding-a-ding-a-ding-a-dong-ding.
Will you come? Will you not?
Will you find my chimney pot?
I hope Santa Claus will come tonight.

Through the year I've tried to do
The kinds of things you'd want me to
And I can only hope
That you have seen me trying.
Now that we've reached Christmas night
I hope you'll find my house all right
And in your sack of toys
I hope there's one just for me.

Santa, if you're about,
Please don't go and miss me out.
I hope Santa Claus will come tonight.
Ding-a-ding-a-ding-a-ding-dong-ding.
Ding-a-ding-a-ding-a-ding-dong-ding.

A Christmas dream

Debbie Campbell

A♭7
G7
C
long red dress.' 'Well,' said San-ta, 'guess I'd bet-ter con-fess. I'm a
Am
D7
fe-male San-ta, that's the rea-son why I've got no whis-kers and my
G
D
G
D/A
G
voice is high.' She turned to go with a 'Ho, Ho, Ho, It's
A♭7
G7
C
e-qual op-por-tu-ni-ties now you know.' And when I en-quired what
D7
hap-pened to San-ta She re-plied, 'He re-tired.' And then she be-gan To

G
A♭7
turn to go with a 'Ho, Ho, Ho, It's e - qual op - por - tu - ni - ties

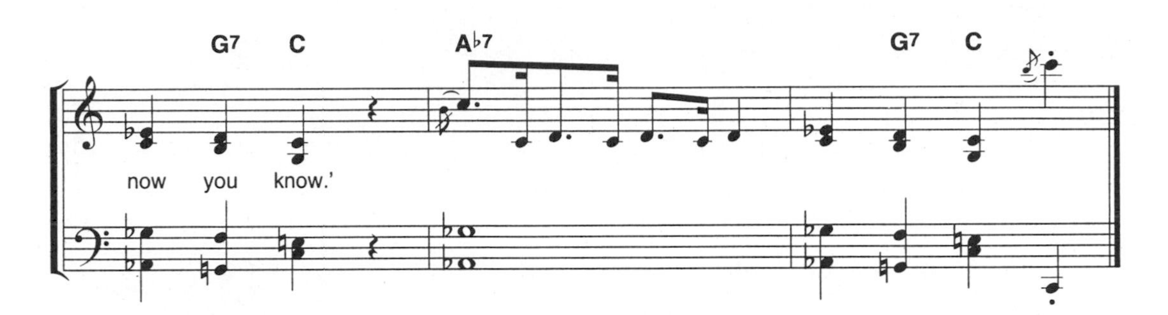
G7 C
A♭7
G7 C
now you know.'

I can't get to sleep

Debbie Campbell

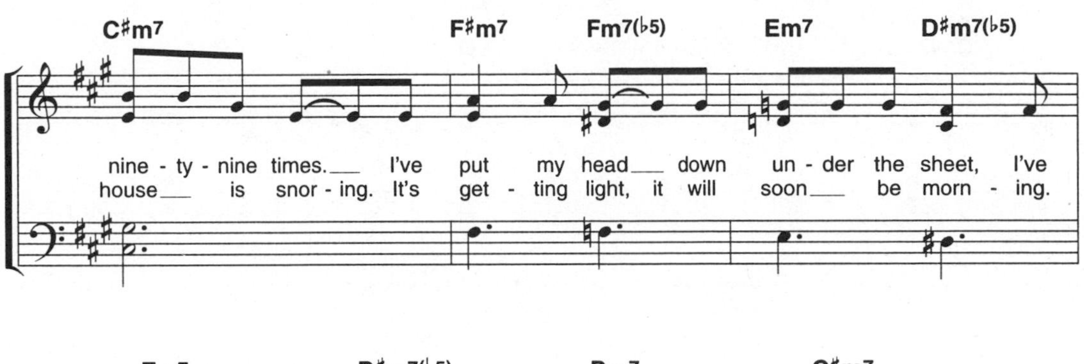

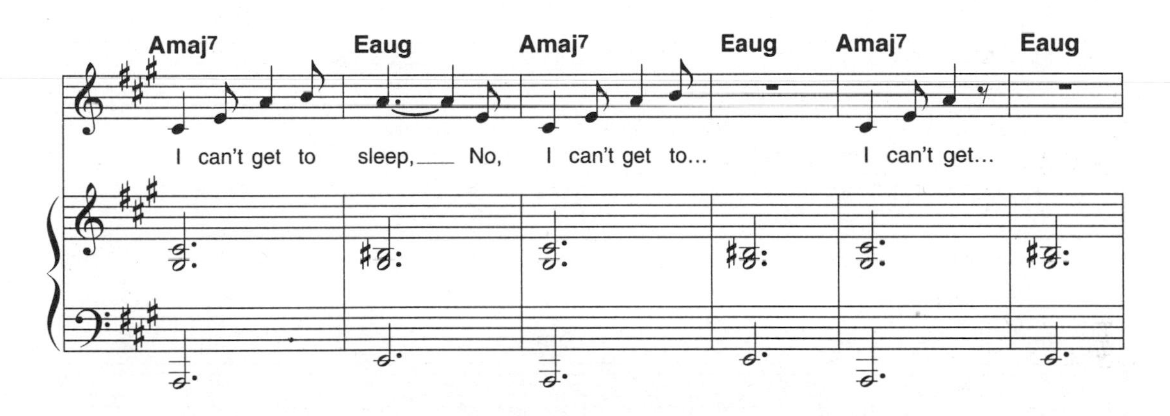

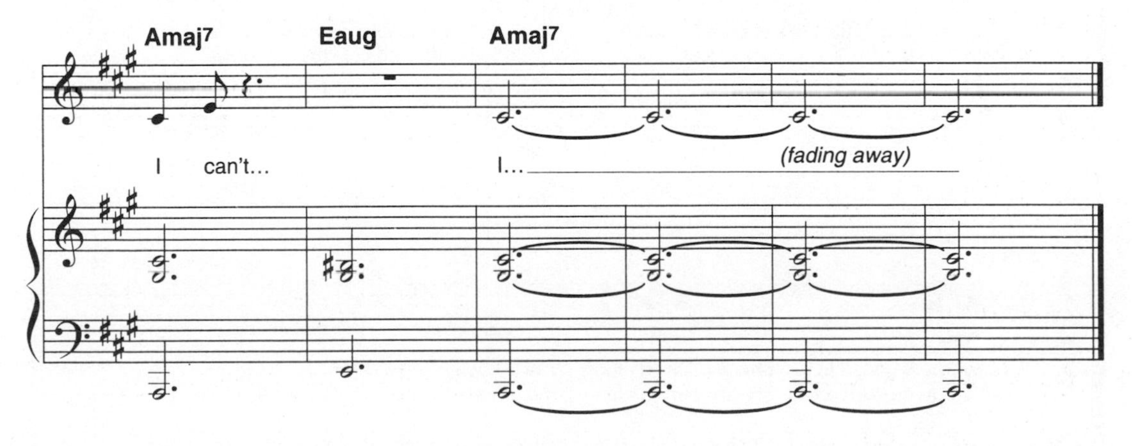

Use wood blocks for the ticking clock and chime bars for the striking clock.

If I stay awake

Clive Barnwell

2.
F
G
C
way.
And if I stay a - wake,
may - be I'll see
C6
Dm
San - ta Claus
With his big white beard
and suit of
G
C
red.
If I can stay a - wake
may - be I'll see
C6
Dm
G
San - ta Claus,
Though I know that he'll on - ly come when I'm fast a - sleep in
C
F/C
G
C
bed.

Merry Christmas and a Happy New Year!

Chris Williams

Divide singers into five groups. Let the ground group start. (They repeat these two bars until the end.) Group 1 starts after a couple of turns of the ground. Group 2 starts as group 1 moves to the second line and so on. Conductor indicates a big rit. to end and each group ends on the last note of the line they are singing.

Christmas pudding song

Ian Henderson Begg

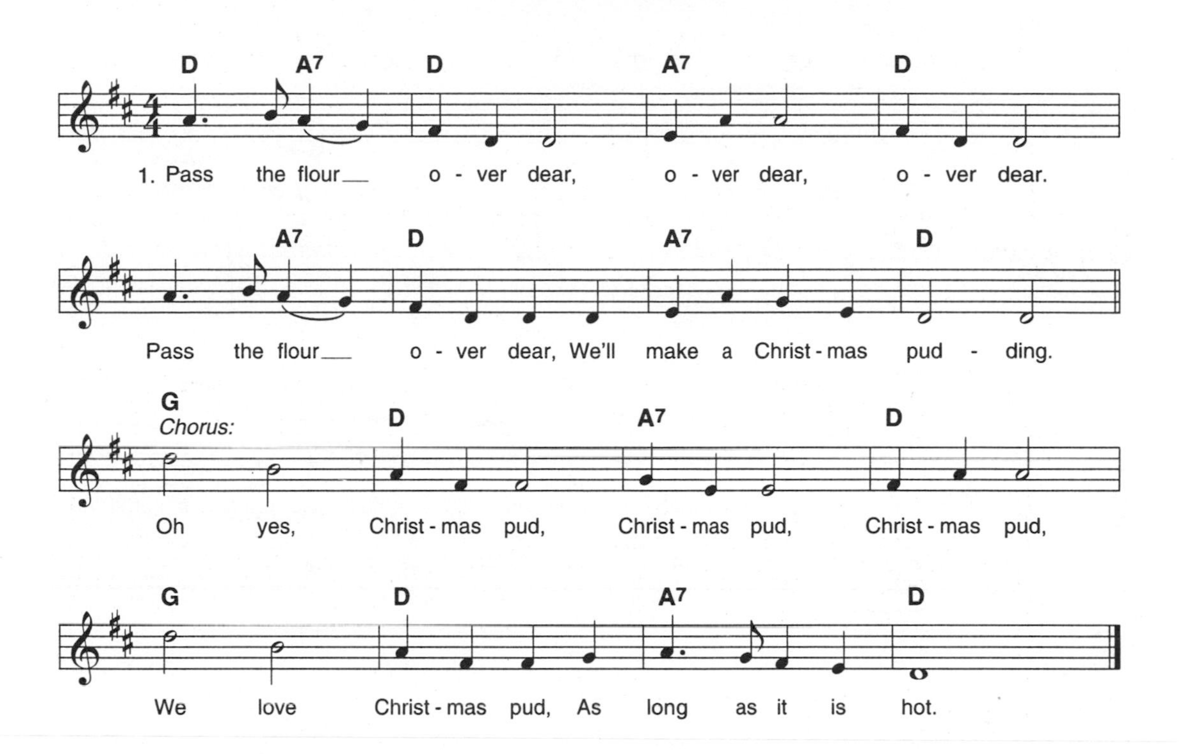

2.Pass the suet over dear... etc.
3.Pass the sugar over dear... etc.
4.Pass the spices over dear... etc.
5.Raisins and sultanas next, tanas next, tanas next etc.
6.Break the eggs in, crack and splat, crack and splat etc.
7.Last we'll add some candied peel, candied peel etc.
8.Mix it up and make a wish, make a wish etc.

After-dinner lament

Lisa Mackenzie

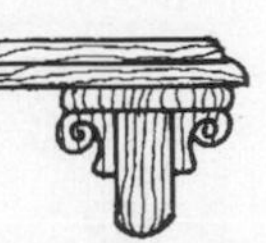

2.Grandma's washing up the dishes,
Dad picks the crackers off the floor,
Mother's running round with Christmas pud and brandy,
But we couldn't eat a single sausage more, oh no!

Chorus

3.Uncle Terry's rather tipsy!
Sis says she's gained a stone or more;
Mother's rushing round with petits fours and coffee,
But we couldn't eat a single sausage more, oh no!

Chorus

4.Auntie's switching on the telly,
A really good film on Channel Four;
Mother's rushing round with indigestion tablets,
But we couldn't eat a single sausage more, oh no!

Chorus

Wishing you all a merry Christmas

Clive Barnwell

2.Christmas time, we are all excited
And watching Advent candles lighted.
We'll make the Christmas tree shine bright.
Christmas season has come.

Christmas time, we are all enchanted
When Christmas trees are bought and planted.
We'll make the Christmas tree shine bright.
Christmas season has come.

Chorus

New Year

Music by Peter Morrell and words by Elizabeth Chapman

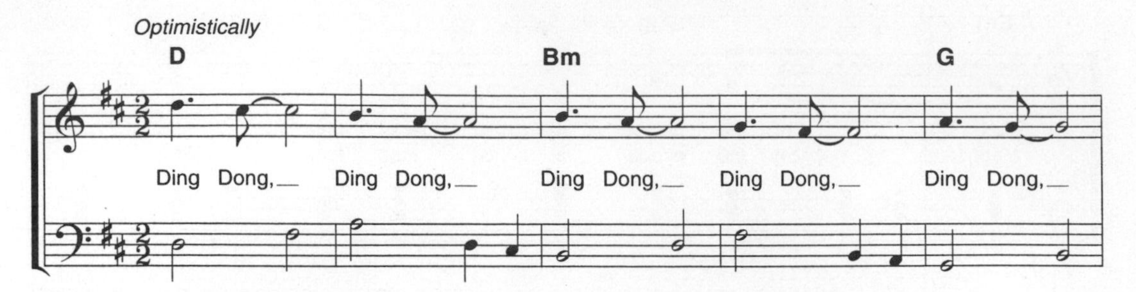

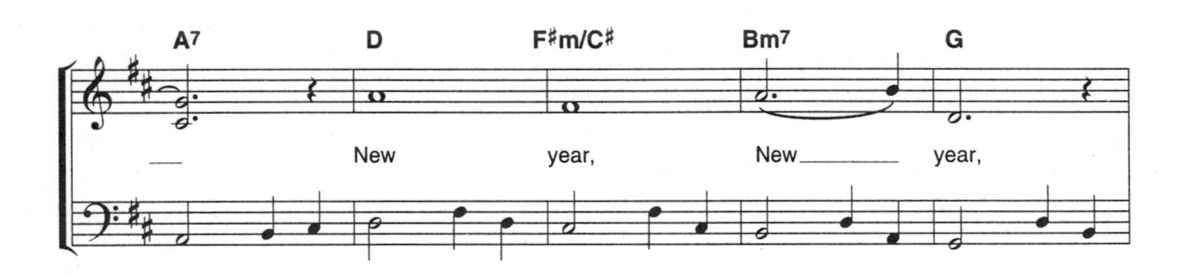

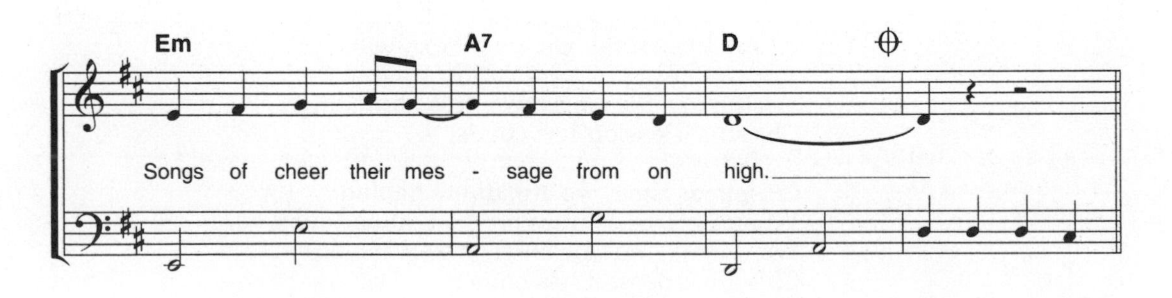

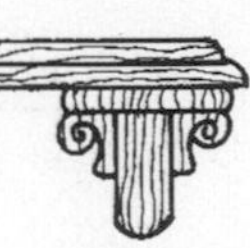

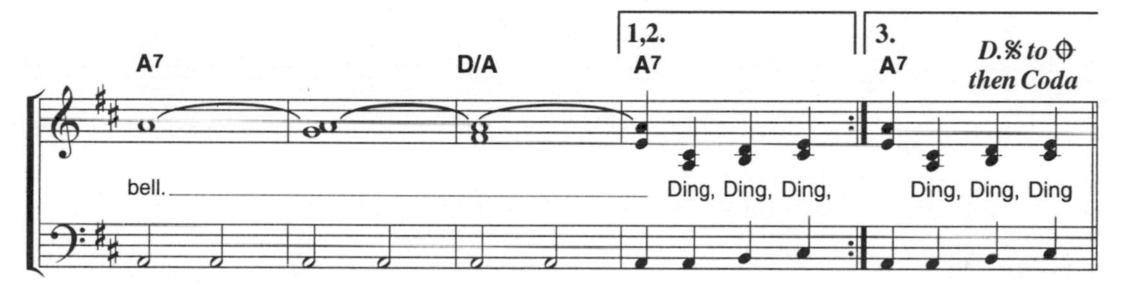

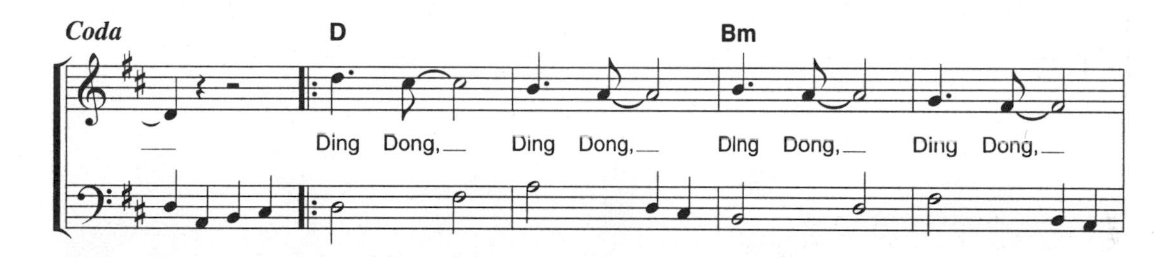

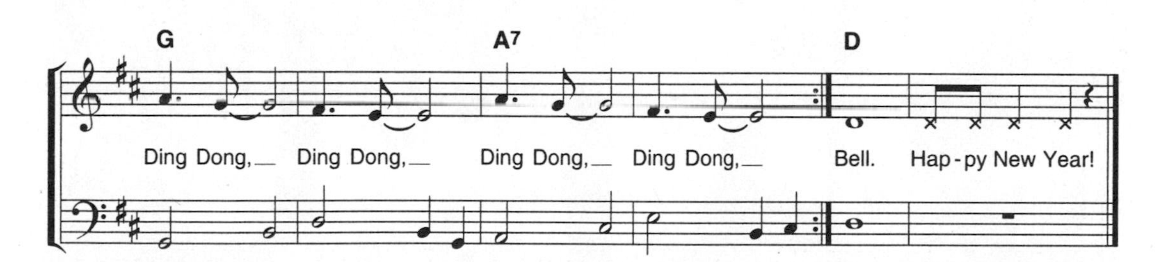

2.Peering through the chilly darkness
Can we see a light?
Will it lead us shining forward
Or return us to the night?

Chorus

3.So we step into the New Year
Following the chimes,
Hopeful future lies before us,
Joy and gladness, magic times.

Chorus

Ding Dong, Ding Dong, Ding Dong, Ding Dong,
Ding Dong, Ding Dong, Ding Dong, Ding Dong. HAPPY NEW YEAR!

Christmas bells

Gillian Parker

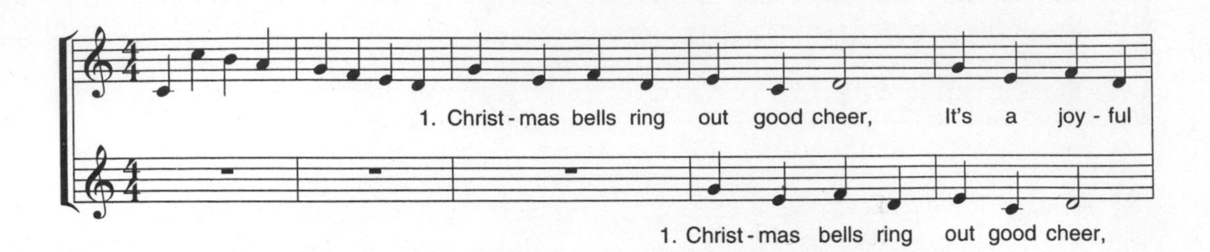

2.Silent snowfall in the night,
Wake up in a world so white.

Chorus

3.Hang the tinsel on the tree,
Shining bright for all to see.

Chorus

4.Christmas bells ring out good cheer,
It's a joyful time of year.

Chorus

Ostinato

This simple ostinato figure of two bars can be played throughout on chime bars and/or glockenspiels, representing bells pealing. The melody is for unison voices or can be sung in two parts, the first four bars as a canon.

Index of First Lines